THE YEAR OF THE RAT

THE YEAR
OF THE RAT

A CHRONICLE

MLADIN ZARUBICA

HARCOURT, BRACE & WORLD, INC.

NEW YORK

This book, with my love, is for

ANITA

who knows

and for

KARYN, SHAWNE, TADD, DARRYL, and FIONN

so that someday they will know

About the Author

Mladin Zarubica, whose name is a heritage from his Yugoslavian parents, is a native-born American who spent his youth in southern California. He attended U.C.L.A. and was graduated in 1939. He managed to combine his studies with athletics and played tackle on the varsity football team with such success that he won an Honorable Mention in the United Press All-American nominations.

He served in the United States Navy from 1941 through 1945 and was released from active duty at the end of World War II as a senior lieutenant. During the war he served on, and eventually commanded, motor torpedo boats, his principal duty being on PT 360 of Squadron 27 attached to the Third and Seventh Pacific Fleets. His tour with the PT's covered a twenty-seven-month campaign in the southwest Pacific, ranging all the way from Guadalcanal to Manila Bay. Lieutenant Zarubica, in command of PT 360, spearheaded the American naval forces into Manila Bay.

From 1945 through 1948 he was a regional manager for the Austria–Southern Germany division of the Coca-Cola Export Corporation, his main task being the construction of new plants and the commencement of their operations. In 1948 he returned briefly to the United States, then took a post on the overseas staff of the National City Bank of New York. He spent almost two years in Montevideo, Uruguay, in the banking business, surveying business firms and preparing the bank's monthly economic report on Uruguay. He returned to New York to become an account executive with Bozell and Jacobs, Inc., working primarily on a public information program for the electric light and power industry. In 1954 he was assigned to an extension of this program in California, his home state. By the end of that year he had co-founded a heavy-construction firm. He has lived in California ever since, and now resides in Los Angeles with his wife, Anita, a native San Franciscan, and their five children.

At the conclusion there will be no doubt in the reader's mind why, after a certain day early in January 1959, Mladin Zarubica was compelled to write this book.

PART I

Carlo

1

I will always remember the setting, the desolate, remote mountain wilderness, the rocky Alps dense with cold, wintry forests. The occasion was my first hunting trip into Bavaria. I could have gone to one of several places, but I chose Erlot's lodge. Surely, as the great door of the hunting lodge swung open to me that evening, I did not suspect I was crossing so strange a threshold, one that would lead into the violent past, into a fascinating tale of desperate adventure, and quite possibly into an unrecorded footnote to history.

To be sure, we had been driving across the very stage of history for some hours. We had headed south toward Salzburg, my companions and I, in two canvas-topped jeeps loaned to us by the U.S. Army. I was looking forward to this weekend hunting trip, a respite from my all too demanding assignment of building an industrial plant for the Coca-Cola Export Corporation, a structure in size capable of producing soft drinks for the entire city of New York.

Not too many months ago I had been released from active wartime duty with the U.S. Navy in the Pacific, had hung up my uniforms and my commission, and promised myself a peaceful existence with my wife in some happy place far removed from the war. Yet here I was in Austria, surrounded by the physical scars of battle, plunged into a psychological atmosphere where everyone avoided mention of and thus emphasized awareness of recent enmity, and with my wife thousands of miles away at home in America. Well, it was a challenging job and only a temporary one, my wife was soon to join me, and, since my forebears had come from lands not far away, I was personally fascinated by this journey.

On this afternoon in the early fall of 1946, some of the trees in the rolling countryside were already bare. The sparse golden leaves that still clung to the aspen trees trembled in the wind, while their fallen companions already lay so thick along the winding Salzburgerstrasse that they all but covered the cobblestone curbs and sidewalks.

We had skirted the northeast section of the city. The castle in Salzburg, with its formidable battlements, overlooked the city. Could one sense the ancient crosscurrents of human settlements that had existed here? When the Romans swept across and conquered this land, it was already inhabited by the Celts. After the fall of the Roman Empire, Austria became a border province of Charlemagne's empire. Time had played out many extraordinary chapters here—and some not so long past.

A turn in the road brought into view the long, upswept vista toward the mountains, cold and magnificent in the distance. We were headed directly for the toe of one towering Alp, the Watzmann.

As we began to ascend from the low basin into the mountain belt, grazing cattle appeared in the autumn mist. We drove on into the village that had once been the headquarters of the infamous Schutzstaffel, Hitler's elite guard, the black-uniformed S.S. Corps. Our light jeeps skidded onto what seemed an endless stretch of massive asphalt. I could not feel a flaw in the roadbed.

Not a soul was visible along the highway. We were on what had once been Hitler's private road, used for his journey by armored car between Berchtesgaden and heavily guarded airstrips near the outskirts of Salzburg. This asphalt speedway was four lanes wide, straight as an arrow, with a half-mile clearing on either side of it. I could almost visualize the marshaled guards extending the full length of the highway on both sides. This line had protected the Fuehrer from attempts on his life.

It was about three in the afternoon when we came into Berchtesgaden. We were in the American Occupation Zone; a U.S. Military Police sign set the speed limit at fifteen miles per hour. We drove slowly past a double gate that had once guarded the entrance to Berchtesgaden Schloss, now headquarters for the American Military Government. The two jeeps moved through Berchtesgaden, descended into a small, deep valley just below the town, and then began to climb up the other side of the valley. Below was nothing but gray, dark houses embraced by the mist of the gathering dusk. As we turned sharply we came upon an unimposing sign: THE BERGHOF, HITLER'S OFFICIAL ALPINE RESIDENCE.

The road cut through tall pine and larch trees and brought us face to face with the ruins of the dark, destroyed Berghof, still a half-mile distant. It had been undamaged by the devastating R.A.F. raid on the S.S. headquarters nearby; however, the S.S. Corps itself had managed to raze it, just before American units entered Berchtesgaden.

The Berghof had been planned as a structure of stone that fitted in with the natural surroundings. Even though it was now rubble, one could see it had been a fantasy place, a work of fine masonry resting upon a gentle slope of that tremendous mountain range. High above this retreat was the famous observation platform built as a private lookout for Hitler.

Our jeep came up on the Berghof's main terrace, still majestic, facing out across the Bavarian Alps, with a view that extended beyond Germany into Austria.

In such surroundings, it is easy for the mind to range. I thought of earlier days when Hitler might have stood here on the terrace, the madman conjuring an insane dream of world conquests. He had plunged a good part of the world into a monstrous barbarism, yet before death rescued him from a more severe retribution he had seen his dream die under the most staggering counterassault ever launched. Small consolation to us for such grievous harm, but consolation.

5

Berchtesgaden must have had special significance for Hitler. A scant thirty miles to the north lay the small town of Braunau where he was born, the son of a minor customs official who died when Adolf was thirteen. His mother was devout and quiet, a timid woman who dedicated herself and her child to the Holy Virgin. Yet not even this early and sincere dedication prevented his growth into one of the most sinister men our civilization, or any civilization, has known.

It is a trifle more than a hundred miles from Braunau, in Austria, to Munich, in Germany. A pale young man, frail and morose, made that apparently insignificant journey not so very long ago. Yet the world will long remember the ultimate horror that resulted from the fateful journey that so began in the early nineteen-twenties when Hitler left the little town. What if he had remained in Braunau? What indeed, I thought, as I turned away from the panoramic view on the lofty terrace. An idle speculation; he had gone from Braunau to Munich, and from Munich to the very core of hell.

2

It was quiet in the frosty, graying dusk as we turned into the densely forested valley, losing sight of the Alps about us. The air smelled of pine, as clear, cold mountain air can in the heart of autumn. About two miles down the road, we turned into a small clearing. In its center, bordered by pine trees, stood a large dark Tyrolean mountain lodge.

I wondered how our Austrian hosts would receive us. In 1946 very few foreign travelers came into the Tyrol, and there were no public areas for hunting. Each hunting party had to be accompanied by an official hunter, a "Jaeger" appointed by Austrian authorities. Most of these guides had been trained in the baronial tradition of hunting. Erlot, the chief Jaeger for the region, appointed deputies to assist his hunting parties.

We parked in the clearing in front of the lodge and prepared to move our gear indoors. The main door of the lodge opened, and a large, well-built man appeared, a black silhouette against a background of orange light. On his command, two figures appeared and were almost instantly at our sides ready to help. He spoke to them in a penetrating voice that pierced the evening air like a foghorn. His greeting in German was hale and friendly. Meanwhile his men carried in our supplies—coffee, food, whisky, cigarettes, and cigars, all difficult items for an Austrian or a German to obtain.

After my companions had introduced me to Herr Erlot, we entered the large main hall of the lodge. Now, in the light, I saw the rugged face of the lodgekeeper. He was a fiery-eyed, immense man, a hardy mountaineer, toughened by time and much living out of doors.

He wore a heavy, tweedy suit, which looked slept in, with leggings stuffed into hobnailed boots and the traditional Tyrolean hat. Over his leather vest lay a heavy watch chain.

Frau Erlot appeared, greeted everyone, and hurried off. Erlot offered schnapps, a welcome antidote to the cold. One of my companions asked about the hunting. The elusive chamois was considered difficult game, a challenge to sportsmen the world over.

"As good as the hunter," Erlot answered. "Some of you may leave with the chamois beard, the Gamsbart. When you see this on the hat of a hunter, you know he has brought down his chamois."

He explained that the wind in the morning would be the key to success. Our guides were the best and he was expecting a good hunt; the heavier snows above the crestline would tend to force the chamois farther down the ridges in greater numbers.

Supper included the noodles we had brought and which Frau Erlot cooked with deer liver, a dish resembling beef Stroganoff. This was accompanied by our American beer. We had had a long drive and since our Jaegers would arrive about 4:45 A.M. the next morning ready for the hunt, we retired early.

When I arose the bitterly cold Bavarian morning chilled me to the bone. We gathered in the main hall, the only warm room in the lodge. We found four Jaegers drinking hot black coffee with Erlot. They were wearing dark, heavy green coats, pants with leggings, and the Tyrolean hunters' hats, all exhibiting the chamois beard.

Breakfast was hot black coffee and generous portions of freshly baked rolls, passed on a big tray by Frau Erlot.

I have a lasting impression of the hunting guides. They sat with the casual look of men who await each day for whatever the Fates decree. Of the four, one sat more silent than the rest.

Because of his manner, my attention focused upon him. The guides seemed caught up in the enthusiasm of the hunt, easily recounting events of other hunts. All except the one.

He was a striking figure; short-legged and with the build of a squatty giant. His large head was crowned by a mane of receding, straight black hair, slightly grayed at the temples, which was badly in need of a haircut. He had a round, large-featured face, with puffy circles below his eyes. He was one of the hardiest-looking men I had ever seen. I asked Erlot what his name was. He answered, "Carlo."

The group was discussing the chances for the hunt. The extreme cold was favorable; so too was the lack of updraft mountain winds, which might carry the scent of the hunter to the quarry.

It was Herr Erlot who finally stood up from the table. He looked every bit a hunter with his hobnailed boots, tightly strapped waist, and the pack he was even then flinging on his back. He finally whistled shrilly. With a sigh, two of the guides rose, stretching their arms. The morning promised a routine venture for them. They obviously did not cherish this hunt as I did. We filed out into the pitch darkness and the biting cold.

The art of silence is probably the most important lesson to learn in hunting chamois. Walking must be a near-soundless act. The hunting party moved uptrail with care, looking like a row of ghosts in the fog.

I watched Carlo closely and saw that, with each step, the lead leg was raised high and the foot lowered slowly on its toes, spreading the foliage with hardly a rustle. We passed through dense forest and difficult thicket in a surprisingly short time. We moved along a narrow, winding trail, fairly high up on the mountainside. The valley below was only a tabletop of dark, cold morning mist.

When we had reached the summit the group dispersed into individual parties. I drew Carlo and followed him quietly off to a narrow, winding ledge.

After we had walked some forty minutes, Carlo stopped. He raised his hand and held it toward me to capture my full attention.

"Wait here," he said in a hushed tone.

He moved soundlessly out of sight. After perhaps three minutes I saw the outline of Carlo's bulky figure, his bull-like neck and the large head that protruded above it. He motioned me forward.

"Chamois. Quiet!"

For all his heavy appearance, he could move quickly. I followed him some forty paces to a higher open ledge, where the wind stung. Looking along Carlo's point, I saw several chamois with their young as they emerged above some large, broken rocks about four hundred yards ahead. I knew we must pick a buck carefully, for they had been grazing there long enough for the young to have mingled with the elders.

Carlo motioned again for silence. He had been kneeling; now he rose slowly and turned toward me. I knew that the moment for my first, and possibly only, shot of the morning was at hand. A disquieting thought had crossed my mind: It would have been impossible for me to hunt—or even to exist—little more than one year ago in the Bavarian Alps.

I waited, and watched Carlo for instructions. He handed me the field glasses and whispered, "Buck, third from right."

I looked through the heavy field glasses and could see a large buck at the shelf's edge. I can remember the sense of excitement. To stalk and drop a buck chamois was a considerable accomplishment.

Carlo cautioned me to wait, and peered again through the large gray binoculars; they were quite unlike any I had ever seen before. Suddenly the chamois were soaring over the crags above. Away they went, jumping and swerving from crag to crag. I thought we were losing them.

It seemed that the chamois's footing surely must give way as they leaped along the canyon wall, veering dizzily above the chasm, a thousand feet or more straight down. Carlo motioned me on and we moved rapidly from one ledge to another. I cannot estimate how far we strode, down and up, along that windswept Alp. I think it must have been about forty minutes before Carlo stopped abruptly and pointed.

In the distance small specks appeared to be moving slowly; they were too far off for a shot. Just then the least expected thing happened. A welcome wind swept down toward us; our scent would not be detected. The chamois began to move toward us on a ledge about seven hundred yards away, sometimes stopping, then moving with their graceful, incredible swiftness. Two bucks led the herd to within about three hundred yards from where we stood. Carlo and I remained rigid. Had the wind shifted to bear a taint of man in the air, we would never have seen them again.

As I stood waiting for Carlo's move, the chamois, bunched together, grazed along a precipitous cliff in a small pocket. I could not imagine what he was waiting for. Later he explained he was waiting for them to group properly for a clear and safe shot.

Carlo now motioned to me. In the morning light, I took careful aim through my rifle sight. I estimated the range at about two hundred and fifty yards, the chamois having moved off to the right from their previous position. Carlo gave me the signal to fire; I squeezed the hair trigger; the rifle responded. I heard the crack and the shrill report that resounded from wall to wall, down into the folds of the mountain. I saw two chamois hesitate like frozen figures, looking for the lead buck they could not now see.

Carlo said, "Quiet!" and motioned me to stand still.

He aimed higher and at a range far greater than mine. Another buck had appeared on the higher level, standing there for not more than three or four seconds. Carlo fired. His buck seemed to drop simultaneously with the shot. I dreaded moving ahead; I suspected I had failed. Nevertheless, I quickly joined Carlo.

"Good shot," he said. "Come, I will lead you." He glanced at me over his shoulder. "You now see why the chamois is one of the greatest prizes for the hunter."

We started ahead, climbing now at a much faster pace. We were both anxious to see our score. My anxiety grew greater as each moment passed. As we neared the rock ledge where I hoped my prize lay, I could see that Carlo felt no fatigue. I thought what a dangerous and deadly adversary he would be in these surroundings. Much as I admired his prowess at the hunt, he gave me an uneasy feeling.

I had witnessed a cool and calculated stalk of prey. Carlo had performed with such precision that I felt sure he could do this as easily again, any time. It was unlike any hunting I had ever experienced. I was suddenly aware that, for him, the result was foregone. He was as close to a professional killer as any person I had ever met. Now Carlo moved quickly toward the scene where my buck would be.

It was there. Standing beside it, Carlo fumbled momentarily in his coat pocket, drew out a good-sized knife, and slit my chamois from the gizzard to the navel.

"Congratulations," Carlo said, and adroitly cleaned out the entrails. He grinned. "I think we must go up higher to see what we have there, no?"

He turned and started climbing. As we moved along the rocky ledge, he said several words in German that I did not understand until he came to the last word "schön," which I knew meant fine. He pointed down, then jumped to the next ledge, six feet below. He drew off his gun sling and rifle and, before I realized it, was cleaning the second buck.

I will never forget how cold that morning was—my muscles ached. Carlo and I were headed back to the lower valley, our bucks slung shoulder to shoulder on two neatly prepared

12

branches carried between us like a stretcher. The hike back was invigorating. There was a green-misted calm in that beautiful morning scene. There was no sound except for the far-off echoes of the farmers plowing the dark rich soil, preparing to trap the rain which was certain to fall at any time. There was little need for anyone to say anything. It had been a good hunt.

3

The great door of the lodge was unlocked. We opened it and, despite our heavy hunting gear, walked in quietly. I do not believe anyone knew we were back.

Carlo sat down in the main hall of the lodge. Its walls were filled with dark, drab oils of bearded, husky Bavarians and, crowded among them, stuffed chamois heads, trophies of past hunts. The black polished floor caught the light of the fireplace, revealing pitmarks from the trampling of innumerable hobnailed boots.

I strolled slowly around the main hall and then sat down across from Carlo. It must have been about nine o'clock in the morning; my companions and their party had not as yet returned. We were two relaxed figures before a roaring fire, in a huge chamber that could easily have held seventy or eighty people.

"It's a fine old lodge, Carlo. Have you been here long?" I asked in English.

Carlo answered me in his stilted English, often resorting to a German word or phrase, until we discovered, undoubtedly because of my name, that we could converse easily in Serbo-Croatian, the language of Yugoslavia. My parents had taught me and, from the time I was very young, I was at home in both English and Serbian. Where Carlo had learned I do not know.

"I have spent time here, but only since the war have I been a Jaeger. No time to hunt when there is war. No time for anything."

"Were you in the Nazi Army?" I asked.

He appraised me coolly and I had the momentary impression he was not going to answer, but he responded.

"Before Hitler dissolved it, I was in the Abwehr."

"Your secret service?"

"Our military intelligence."

"And then?"

"After 1944 I transferred to the security police."

"Wasn't that part of the S.S.?"

"After the Abwehr, Himmler took charge of all military intelligence and police affairs. Yes, the security police was made part of the S.S."

"A wonder you were not held as a war criminal, being in the S.S.," I said, and then, realizing how offensive the remark was, I added a smile.

Carlo gave me a quick look, as if to see whether antagonism lay behind my remark. Then, apparently satisfied, he concentrated on lighting his cigar.

During the silence that followed, Frau Erlot entered with fresh, steaming coffee. She appeared passive; she poured the coffee, tended the fire, but she took no apparent interest in our conversation.

I turned to Carlo and said, "Strange. Here we are, an American and a German, hunting chamois. A year ago, we might have been hunting each other. I'm glad it's over."

"For you it's over," Carlo said, "but it will be many years before our country will be the old Germany again."

"Do you mean the old Germany or the Nazi Germany?" I asked.

"A little of both, I think. You know only the bad side because it ended in chaos. Germany needed strong leadership, but we lost the truth somewhere."

"There's always some point where you can still turn back."

Carlo shrugged. I decided that, if I wanted to learn anything from him, I had better not expound my views as strongly as I felt them; but I couldn't help commenting, "You picked a bad leader and an even worse ideology."

"We all knew that, in time."

He placed heavy emphasis on the last words and then let the thought hang.

"Then it's true that few people believed in Hitler at the last?"

"Why do you think the war was allowed to continue when most intelligent Germans knew there was no hope left of winning? Why toward the end was total destruction risked, almost invited?"

His short, bulky figure, still relaxed, rested to one side in the large leather chair. He seemed to weigh the possibility of an answer to his own question, then went on.

"Germany became a strong power because of its military establishments and resources. The military-minded Germans felt that, to become a great nation, they had to fight a great war with success. This would establish Germany as the leader nation. For them to accept defeat was to acknowledge the pointlessness of life. They could not accept it even though they saw it."

"But surely even such minds, reluctant as they were to accept defeat, would recognize it when it was overwhelmingly evident. How could an intelligent people, like the other Germans, thrust children—fourteen, fifteen years old—into the roles of soldiers? All hope must surely have been gone by then."

I must have hit hard. He made no attempt to answer me. What am I doing, I wondered, seeking information or trying to provoke this man?

"Well," I said, "I'm glad I don't have the job of judging the German nation."

Carlo turned his face toward me; his expression was quizzical and, I thought, touched with mockery.

"Suppose I agreed with you. What could a lone man, with or without a gun, do against the highly developed machinery of Nazism?"

"Enough lone men could have stopped it," I said.

"Maybe in the beginning; not later. But everybody was behind Hitler at first. He made Germany into a nation—Autobahns, schools, industry. He handed the German back his nationalism."

Then, abruptly, Carlo gave a small twisted smile.

"You Americans stopped the best the Nazis had, the mightiest mass of arms the world has ever seen, and yet eventually you strengthened the Communists. Why didn't you continue to the East with your armor, and finish the Soviets? Have you forgotten the Soviets were *our* allies in 1939, when we got our real start?"

I looked at Carlo, and saw in him the failings of the Nazis. Carlo's kind of reasoning seemed an essential ingredient in any form of totalitarian government; the Soviets had also shown their scorn for treaties except as a means to disguise their true intention. I answered him pointedly.

"In a sense, Carlo, when it comes to Communists, I admit you have a tempting premise. As far as I'm concerned, I see very little difference between the Nazis or the Communists. The slogans are about the same—just twisted and turned a bit. The rationales are different, but the ends amount to the same thing —subjugation of people and a greed for land and power. In time, we may very well wish we had continued on East. But we are bound by honor—or, if you scoff at that term, we are bound by our pledged word. We abide by our treaties."

Carlo shifted his husky frame to the other side of the chair and said, with an air of studied authority, "Yes, there are many parallels between Nazism and Communism. The Communists are treating religion in the same way that Hitler did. Hitler removed religion from the people; there could be no divided ultimate loyalty. Germany was all, and Hitler was Germany. God was not German, but universal. This concept the Fuehrer had to kill, and replace with his twentieth-century Nazi glory.

17

He wooed the German multitudes with ritualistic pageants and they shouted back, 'Heil Hitler!' And finally he was crazed by their adulation, and became reckless."

He paused, watching me for some reaction. I said, "Recklessness was your philosophy."

He raised his arm, pointing his index finger at me, and said mockingly, "And what about America's reckless voyage with Communism? I can tell you that German intelligence, back in 1935, knew that Communists had infiltrated many of your governmental agencies. One of the basic Communist policies was to turn your democracy against Nazism to protect the Soviet, and this was carried out through hundreds of popular-front organizations and societies. Wasn't the Soviet government at last diplomatically recognized during this period of American lethargy? Once they had diplomatic recognition, the road was paved for their wider subversive operations, for infiltration by thousands of Soviet agents who come as recognized officials— the trade missions, consular clerks, and diplomatic officials. And do you think they have stopped? Do you think that today, in America, the Soviet underground operates less intensely, less destructively?"

This was the circular argument of principle opposed to expediency, of material gain opposed to moral loss, of momentary glory opposed to historical damnation, of rationalization in a too complex world. Perhaps politics, as has been suggested, is the art of the possible, but casual conversation between two recent enemies concerning international politics is very nearly impossible. I thought I might shift the subject.

"Carlo, sitting in this peaceful spot, I find it hard to believe that there was so much devastation here."

"There are many things you would find hard to believe." The same twisted smile, the mocking glance returned. He paused. "There were outrageous mistakes, carefully concealed from the world, that were made within the Third Reich."

18

Again he paused, seeming to deliberate whether he should follow this line of thought. "I know that what I say will not change the world's judgment, nor help the dead cause of the German nation's war effort. But as the Third Reich grew, the key men who occupied the real posts of command were the 'beer-hall politicians.' In time, these men publicly assumed the roles of statesmen and leaders of the Reich. The Nazi state grew but respect for the people in high government places did not."

Carlo went on to describe how Adolf Hitler's stance as party leader, his military tone and solemnity, were often shattered by his wild rages when he faced his party followers—as at Nuremberg, when, with the frenzy of a tyrant, he would shout out across the endless field, *"Obedience!"*

The only response from those multitudes that had joined in this fanatical ritual was a massive thunder of "Heil Hitler! Heil Hitler! Sieg heil! Sieg heil!" They shouted it for hours on end.

Carlo stopped for a moment, remembering, then added, "Hitler had madder dreams than the world could have guessed —he was obsessed by them."

I looked intently at Carlo. He sensed my keen interest and said, "For the last year of the war, particularly the last eight months, a week hardly passed without a press source quoting Hitler, or someone in his entourage, as referring to the miracle weapons. Do you know what they were?"

I shook my head. Carlo's face hardened. "Gas, germ warfare. The V weapons and jet planes were Hitler's other toys, but germ warfare and gas intrigued him."

There was a long pause, while I looked at Carlo in complete disbelief. "That seems too evil even for the Nazis."

"Hitler did not proceed because of the resistance from Rundstedt, Rommel, Speidel, and the others. The majority of the General Staff was against it. As a matter of fact, all of the generals in Rommel's camp were opposed to it. And Rommel was the German people's great hero, practically the only one of such high rank Hitler permitted to exist with so much adulation. Rommel—there was a man."

I could sense Carlo was about to launch into a story and I listened closely to each word.

"Rommel had the instincts of a true soldier. He knew that the decision in the West was imminent. He had requested an audience with Hitler, who had earlier ordered him to tour the defenses of the Atlantic wall and make a report of his findings. Hitler's whole mind at that time was concentrated on the impending Allied invasion and the defense of the Channel coast against it. And so Hitler approved Rommel's request for a meeting.

"Field Marshal von Rundstedt had on several occasions indicated to Rommel and the others of his staff that the 'mad corporal' would no doubt want to assume full personal command of the armies in the West, just as he had on the Russian front. Rundstedt was desperately concerned; only cool, military decisions could offset complete disaster."

There, in the quiet Bavarian lodge, Hitler suddenly came to life as Carlo depicted him.

"A meeting between Hitler and Rommel was held. Unfortunately, Rommel found Hitler in one of his intensely depressed moods, sunken in sadness, deeply morose. This was usually followed by one of his barbarous fits. Rommel, who had so completely captivated Hitler during the African campaign, was by degrees losing his luster in the Fuehrer's eyes. And, as a military tool, Rommel no longer seemed useful to him. Hitler's mood could change violently in a split second; decisions were revamped as quickly to meet his furious change of heart.

"At the formal meeting, as in preliminary memoranda, Rommel told Hitler that he must change the western strategy from an immobile, total-coast defense to an aggressive, elusive, fast-moving defense that might concentrate, then conceivably withdraw, then assault again with fury. This was, of course, entirely opposed to Hitler's idea of a string of "fortresses" to defend the western front. Hitler began to rage and scream when he heard Rommel's plan, and loudly proclaimed that he would not permit any such withdrawals.

"Hitler's basic plan of fortress defense called for strong resistance points—towns, cities, hastily prepared field defenses—which incorporated, in part, Calais, Cherbourg, Brest, Le Havre, Cap Gris Nez, and Dunkirk. Rommel openly disagreed with this defensive tactic."

Carlo paused to relight his cigar, but I made no move to interrupt. He drew deeply, then continued. "Rommel asked Hitler why he held to the fortress plan and, while Hitler stared at him in a moody silence, quickly added that if the enemy were to break through such a rigid line of stationary defense, incapable of flexibility, it could possibly succeed in a breakout that could not be contained at all. The German forces and reserves could not be regrouped for an adequate defense—and men and material would be doomed within their fortress.

"Hitler suddenly unleashed himself upon Rommel, losing all self-composure and finally coherence. He ended by shouting that germ warfare, and the colorless, odorless gas killer, Tabun, would strangle the enemies' will to fight; that a pall of gloom would fall across the English island the first day after their attempted invasion. He proclaimed the brute power of the new V-1 weapon, and spoke with mystical fervor of the production of jet planes.

"Hitler leaned forward on a large oak table in front of him —both arms straight and rigid, his fists tightly clinched, his face pale. Rommel then said, quite pointedly, that he would have no part of gas or germ warfare, nor, he believed, would the majority of the General Staff. Rommel bluntly stated to Hitler that this was against the covenant of warfare; he called it heinous. This was one of the few times anyone had stood up to Hitler, face to face, and argued.

"Hitler screamed at Rommel, then turned and ranted at the

gathering. His scientists, he said, had determined how life started on this planet; the garbage of the universe had drifted in from outer space, eventually to start the microbe cells, which over millions of years have evolved into plant, animal, and human life as we now know it. Now all this life had to be thinned out to perfect civilization. Hitler then turned on Rommel. 'And you cringe when I tell you that we must use germ warfare! You're a coward, a fool! You lost more than battles in the African campaign!'

"Rommel's bearing did not alter. His cold, dark stare never left Hitler's darting eyes. This further enraged Hitler. Rommel spoke in his crisp, unshaken voice, 'The rumors are true; you are mad!'

"Hitler stepped back, rigid with rage, his face now ashen gray, his eyes two black pits. He stared as if paralyzed. His left arm began to twitch. Rommel then fully realized, for the first time, that Hitler had lost his senses completely. He saw now that Hitler was actually a babbling madman. Hitler turned quickly, and walked out of the meeting, his left arm still twitching.

"The Fuehrer left the room in a shroud of silence. Rommel remained silent, watching the departure of Germany's supreme, omnipotent warlord. Rommel was obviously shaken."

The sounds of men approaching from the yard cut off Carlo's dramatic description. The hunting parties were returning. He said nothing more, but sat watching me quietly.

4

Seven weeks passed before my next trip to Erlot's lodge. I took off by jeep again with one of my staff, and we wound our way up the long mountain road, arriving at dusk in the little clearing that fronted the lodge.

We were warmly greeted as we entered. Frau Erlot showed us to our separate rooms; mine was large and extremely neat, probably not often used. The evening chill had been moderated by the fire in the "Kugelofen," a tiled heater commonly used in Germany and Austria.

I cannot say just what had drawn me back to this lodge. I wanted a change from the daily routine of a well-advancing construction job, a change of scene, a change of faces and voices. The adventure of the hunt? Perhaps, but I was not a passionate seeker after live game, even when it provided food much needed. The serenity of the rugged mountain country? Perhaps, but my recollection of the earlier visit was dominated by the yarn-spinning of the mocking storyteller, Carlo. Another encounter with Carlo, then? Perhaps, for I confess there was something magnetic about this man.

Carlo was a collector of tales and a superb narrator. I could imagine him in some fairly responsible post in German military intelligence, probably at headquarters, piecing together rumor, gossip, items from memoranda, bits of communiqués, fragments from files, confidences from his associates, and building these into dramatic incidents that captured his fancy. How much truth lay in these yarns I had no way of knowing, yet I was impressed with Carlo's intelligence and aware of, even a bit chilled by, his detachment; where I might have expected anger, he showed reserve and cynicism; where I might have looked for shame, I found mockery. Yes, I was intrigued by Carlo and suspected there really was a basis of truth in his tales. Did I flatter myself that, in me, he had found a new and challenging listener —the foreigner, the enemy? That, too, may have been part of the fascination for me. In any event, I had returned to the lodge.

Herr Erlot arrived about an hour later. He offered us some whisky and then asked if I'd mind picking up Carlo in my jeep. I asked Erlot about the weather. In his mixture of German and English, he said, "Mein Herr, the chamois will be feeding if the rain does not come. You may have a good hunt."

As soon as we had drained our glasses, Erlot and I left in the jeep and drove several miles along the road we had traveled earlier that afternoon. It was barely after dusk; a heavy gray mist had fallen over the valley. As we came to a fork in the road, Erlot motioned me to stop. Although I looked carefully through the dense forest, I saw nothing until I was suddenly startled by the bulky outline of Carlo; he had appeared, it seemed, out of nowhere.

Carlo approached with all his paraphernalia fastened neatly to his shoulder, his Tyrolean hat pulled low over his eyes, his face scarcely discernible. Erlot moved to the back of the jeep and Carlo eased into the front seat with me.

"Grüss' Gott, Erlot. Good evening, mein Herr. I welcome your jeep."

"Much better than walking," I said.

We sat stiffly, trying to protect ourselves from the bitter cold as we drove back to the lodge. The wind, whipping in through the open jeep, made it practically impossible to converse, save for some shouted words of caution. By now, darkness had spread over the mountain like a blanket. Our headlights were two frail beams, opening only a small, knifelike cut through the dense darkness.

It was about eight o'clock in the evening when we returned to the lodge. Frau Erlot had supper waiting: a tenderloin of deer meat, prepared with onions; well-flavored brown gravy over boiled potatoes; a dark pumpernickel bread; beer, which had been chilled in a snow pack outside the lodge. Frau Erlot had done well, as always, with the food we had brought.

Conversation remained light and full of good humor, the camaraderie that often comes among hunters. By nine-thirty my traveling companion and Herr Erlot excused themselves and went off to bed. Frau Erlot had long since retired. I was enjoying the quiet, easy atmosphere, watching Carlo, who had remained.

Carlo reached for his glass, lifted it, toasted me with thanks for my gift; I had brought him a box of Havana cigars, a token of my appreciation for his efforts to provide a good hunt. Smoking seemed to give him considerable personal pleasure. He handled the cigar with the air of a connoisseur, openly enjoying himself far more than on our first encounter.

"Have you traveled much?" I asked—the time-honored conversational gambit.

"Most of my time in Germany, but I have traveled elsewhere. In the war I managed to visit some of our occupied countries. I enjoyed my travels."

His last remark was like a physical barb to me. I thought of the tortured souls who had lived through the occupation, and others who had died in it, and I felt an intense dislike for Carlo. Here was no floundering soul caught in the tide of resurgent nationalism. He gave me the impression of a man immune to the terrors and crimes of life, and probably to its miracles. I no longer thought of Carlo as a German; to me he was now a Nazi.

My curiosity had lost that quality of pleasure one finds in seeking to solve a puzzle. My interest was now of an edged sort, the confrontation of an alien and odious mind. Was I reading too much into one single remark? Was I as guilty of harsh and brutal judgment as those I detested? I could not remain silent. "Did your enjoyable travels include sights of the men and women and children starved, turned to flames, or suffocated in gas chambers? Millions of Jews, Poles, Serbs, Czechs—God only knows who and how many? Tell me about your enjoyable travels."

Carlo rubbed his mouth nervously with his huge left hand and for the first time seemed dismayed. Yet he recovered his easy composure with surprising speed. Waving his arm to the northeast, toward Germany, he said, "There are bones out there buried so deep the world will never know—no one will ever know what went on or how! Yet, if Hitler's brain had not been twisted, he could have been as great as Caesar, or even Alexander the Great. This whole European continent could have been neutralized by him and his followers."

I shook my head in negation.

Carlo looked at me owlishly. He seemed to be wondering what I might believe, what he might persuade me to believe. He resembled a defeated revolutionary, grieving for the ruin of his lost cause. In that night's conversation, Carlo expounded the role of the Nazis in the history of the world. He reasoned that Hitler came onto the German scene when the spirit of Germany was flagging and so was able to insinuate his will upon the people, at first by hope, then by promises, then by force, and at last by fear. They became utterly subservient to the Nazi state. As his power became absolute, as Germany became a world force, the policy became hate, not hope. Hitler's grand design was not to make Germany the object of love and admiration, but of dread and hatred. Hitler did not hope for loyalty or pray for co-operation; he commanded devotion and demanded unquestioning obedience. The Master of the Master Race.

"And in the end," I asked, "during those last hours in the bunker, how many of the people around Hitler remained loyal?"

I remember that Carlo was silent for a few minutes. My

question had apparently quieted Carlo, the apologist. Now, abruptly, Carlo, the storyteller carried on.

"There is one incident that is fairly well known. During the last week, when Berlin was about to fall, Hitler summoned Hermann Fegelein, who was married to Eva Braun's sister. He ordered Fegelein to oversee the sealing of all the secret papers, files, and articles of state."

Carlo, the astonishing raconteur, enacted how Hitler had given Fegelein an order. " 'I want you to see that my papers and valuables are sealed in your presence. You, Fegelein, will be sure nothing is removed. All of the documents must be burned.' Fegelein then said, fearing for his own safety, 'Does this mean we are lost, hopelessly lost? My Fuehrer, you must escape! You owe this much to the German people.' "

As Carlo described it, Fegelein lost his composure and pled with Hitler. " 'Escape; you must escape, or we all die!' Fegelein did not know that Hitler had already decided to commit suicide, and was hoping that Hitler would attempt an escape and so save them both. This infuriated the Fuehrer. In booming tones that could be heard outside, he told the cringing Fegelein he could consider himself under immediate house arrest."

Carlo went on to describe the events of the next, fatal day. "Fegelein left the bunker without taking leave of the Fuehrer. When his disappearance was reported, Hitler was so infuriated that he sent a special S.S. patrol to arrest Fegelein—this in spite of the danger from the advancing Russian armies and the deteriorating military situation in Berlin. Hitler had previously issued orders to S.S. General Felix Steiner to counterattack in all sectors without regard to consequences. The Steiner counterattack order was never carried out; Steiner could not even be reached by radio."

Carlo then described how Fegelein was apprehended in his home in the suburbs of Berlin, summarily returned and immediately broken of all rank by the Fuehrer. During these same last hours, Himmler's disloyalty had been disclosed, which sent the Fuehrer into deepest depression. Hitler had Hermann Fegelein executed on the spot, almost as an act of retaliation against Himmler.

Himmler's absence from Berlin during the closing hours of the Third Reich's short history was an unmistakable sign. Now Hitler's suspicions and fears were confirmed. Soon the radio services around the world carried the story of Himmler's attempted peace negotiation through Count Bernadotte of Sweden, and it was in this public manner that the story reached the bunker and the Fuehrer.

Heinrich Himmler, safe from the Fuehrer's retaliation and posing as the acting head of state, offered the Western Allies a surrender. Himmler proposed that the German armies would surrender in the West, but continue fighting in the East until the Western Allies encountered the main Russian force, preferably a good distance east of Berlin. While Himmler and Bernadotte were meeting in Luebeck, Hitler's power held only tenuously with the fragmented army in the field.

Like Himmler, Hermann Goering absented himself from the Berlin trap, the so-called "fortress of Berlin," and offered himself, from a distance of several hundred miles, as Hitler's successor. Goering's telegram read, "Do you agree that I take over total leadership at once?" He proposed that he take over as Hitler's deputy by ten o'clock that same night if no word had been received to the contrary from the Fuehrer. Goering's excuse for his rash move was one of Hitler's old decrees, made during the victorious days of Nazism (it was dated June 29, 1941), in which Goering had been named heir apparent. Hitler now stormed in fury, condemning Goering's act as insurrection and treachery.

"Then, at the last, Hitler really was alone, wasn't he?" I asked Carlo, rephrasing the question that had spurred him to this last narrative. "Apparently, there is no one left who had

28

first-hand knowledge of those last hours in the bunker. Does anyone really know what happened?"

"There are a few who could tell, but they would not. The special unit of the Escort Commandos, standing by in the bunker, they could tell. They were trained to carry out the seven escape plans."

"What were they?" I asked. "I've never heard these plans mentioned before."

"The seven plans that could have saved Hitler from the world that hated him."

I said with sarcasm, "Carlo, I don't believe any plans could have saved Hitler. Suicide was an easy way out for him."

Carlo's shrewd black eyes looked straight at me. He spoke evenly, but with a tone of complete certainty. "Had the Fuehrer chosen any of the seven plans, not a trace of him would ever have been found. He would have remained concealed the rest of his natural life—or until he chose to reveal himself."

Carlo leaned forward. For the next hour and a half he related a fantastic and, I admit, fascinating scheme.

"The seven plans were brilliantly laid out. Anyone could have disappeared from public view in a shroud of mystery and confusion."

The seven plans purportedly took years to perfect. They were the creation of Martin Bormann, the shadowy figure who remained closest to Hitler, yet always out of the world's view. The arrangements took enormous time. Week after week and month after month select groups of men made their way to Bormann's door. Eventually many of these fervent worshipers of the Fuehrer and his cause traveled to far distant parts of the earth. Prior to their departure they were told that they were expendable, and that anyone who dropped the subtlest reference to the plans would be inviting certain extermination; but for these men such hazards made their dedicated mission even more glorious.

29

The first escape plan involved two countries: Bolivia and Paraguay. Bolivia, with its two capitals of La Paz and Sucre, was ideally suited for revolutions. Paraguay, strategically adjacent, was equally susceptible. Within these countries were powerful nationals who were capable of blotting out their governments in an instant's revolution. All they ever required were the necessary funds to underwrite their coups.

Hitler's select guard, known as the S.S. Escort Commandos of the Fuehrer, was capable, under the plan, of leaving by air from any point in Germany, but preferably from near Berchtesgaden. The probable flight plan was over the Alps, cutting across Switzerland, then to the southern coast of France, over the Mediterranean to Africa, and to an airfield in Ruanda-Urundi, a former German colony in Africa given to Belgium after World War I. Ruanda-Urundi is located on the north shores of Lake Tanganyika between the Congo and Tanganyika. Another airfield was to be ready in western Africa. The plan then called for a flight across the southern Atlantic, either for Bolivia or Paraguay. In each country there were two organizations; one was open, the other secret. The first worked through alleged cultural methods, the other by violence and murder. The open front organizations in Paraguay and Bolivia were patterned along the lines of the revolutionary movements, capable of simulating the brand of coup of a fiery people overthrowing a tyranny from within.

The second escape plan had its refueling point in Central Africa. The route was optional. The first option included the same route to Africa that the first plan embraced; the second option, the alternate route, was a flight southeast across Asia Minor, and then across Africa to one of the airfields. From there, the route again led across the South Atlantic, to either Bolivia or Paraguay. The second plan did not call for the overthrow of Bolivia or Paraguay unless it became necessary; rather, at a propitious moment, it called for a transfer to the south of

Argentina. Key figures were well paid for their participation. The payments were made through coded accounts, huge funds secretly held ready in Swiss banks. The payees were kept entirely unaware of the actual source of payment by a system of transfer so guarded as to prevent even inadvertent disclosure.

The third escape plan called for additional optional refueling points, one in East-Central Africa, one in West Africa near the coastal town of Bonda in Gabon. This plan included alternate methods of transport across the South Atlantic; by submarine to southern Argentina, or by air to Bolivia, Paraguay, or southern Argentina. The third plan also provided for an easterly escape from Africa, in which case the flight plan would have taken them into northwestern India. From that point, there were other destinations designated—Tibet and Nepal—had it been deemed necessary.

The fourth escape plan employed the use of several air transports flying different routes. This plan envisioned the grim possibility that the escape party would have an Allied pursuit hot on its trail. Therefore it encompassed a diffusion of planes going east and west, some headed for northwestern India, others for one of the South American countries.

The fifth plan had, again, a possible destination in northwestern India. This plan, however, began with a flight to Portugal, where the escape party would be picked up by submarine and taken across the South Atlantic to a point on the southern Argentine coastal area. Several options were then open to the escape party. They included southern Argentina, Bolivia, Paraguay, or even returning to the West Africa coastal point, from there by air to northwestern India, and then, if necessary, into Tibet.

In each of the seven plans, well-organized underground bands were carefully established like secret Communist cells—in Argentina, Bolivia, Paraguay, Brazil, Africa, India, and China. Although under the authority of the S.S. Escort Commandos of the Fuehrer, they included compromised or defective nationals. They were carefully selected, zealously trained, highly paid, and constantly checked.

The German agents in command and key posts in these undergrounds were able to adapt themselves to the very worst kinds of hardships, and yet many of them were highly professional men in their own specialties. Each group was likely to include a meteorologist, a physician-surgeon, a communications expert, a radio technician, several mechanics, and a core of men one could classify as hardened fighters. They were selected from men of unshakable belief in the Nazi ideals.

None of these teams ever knew that their missions were to afford the Fuehrer an escape from the Third Reich. They believed they had been sent to special areas for certain highly significant missions that would remain undisclosed to them until the time came to carry them out.

The sixth escape plan led to China. This plan was diverse; it had several routes and employed decoy escape teams. One decoy group was to head for Bolivia according to plan one. Another group was to take up secret residence in a rural area of Portugal. They were all to adhere to a strict policy of top secrecy in their movements. All of the S.S. Commando groups were to prepare their bases for the eventuality that the Fuehrer might have to divert his escape route and head for one of their stations. The final destination of plan six was a residence built not too far from Tientsin in eastern China for Hitler's eventual occupancy.

The seventh escape plan was intended to cover even the direst eventualities and called for the boldest stroke. It calculatingly considered that the Fuehrer would find a world entirely hostile to him, a possibility not dismissed by Bormann. Seven escape teams, the elite of the S.S. Escort Commandos of the Fuehrer, were to take off in a fanlike pattern, each headed for one of the following points: Paraguay, Bolivia, Argentina, West Africa, Portugal, northwestern India, and northern China.

Each team would head for its assigned destination approximately thirty days ahead of the Fuehrer. He was eventually to leave for one of the seven points, depending on the situation at the time. Under this plan, all points were to be kept ready to receive Hitler.

Carlo stopped talking, raised his glass and drank deeply, lighted his cigar, stared at me for a moment, and then smiled.

I had been utterly intrigued by his detailed account, masterfully, almost breathlessly told. Now I wondered if he had not been having sport with me, if he had not concocted this fantastic tale. His smile puzzled me.

"Do you really believe this?" I asked.

"Let's say that I think it is a possibility. You too might think it a possibility if you had known Martin Bormann," he replied.

"And you knew him well, Carlo?"

"Ah, no," said Carlo. "I don't believe anyone knew Bormann well. Not even Hitler."

"What happened to him? Was he with Hitler at the end?"

"That is the question the Allied intelligence divisions kept asking. Perhaps they know the answer now. Perhaps not. But it is very late and we are to hunt in the early morning light."

Carlo rose, bowed slightly, and said, "Good night. I hope you were not bored with my stories."

"Good night, Carlo." No, I had not been bored in the least.

5

That weekend passed without my having another solitary encounter with the gifted storyteller. Others were always present with Carlo. I had almost come to the point of asking him a question about the escape plans when I realized that Carlo had never revealed his narrative talent before the group of hunters; indeed, he was a congenially silent member of the company. I let the moment pass, but I wondered if Carlo's reticence about spinning yarns where his countrymen were listeners did not come from a fear of contradiction or of appearing ridiculous. He could indulge himself with me in the certainty that I had no fund of confidential information or depth of knowledge about Germany and could not dispute his account.

I returned to Wels and my job, leaving the lodge and Carlo's fantasies of the Third Reich in the craggy Bavarian Alps.

At a cocktail party in Vienna honoring General Mark Clark, I met Baron Jesse Jesinsky, a member of an old and respected Austrian family. He had spent much of World War II on the Russian front as a major in the German Wehrmacht. His Kammerschloss, on the Traunsee, was one of the most beautiful old castles in Austria. My wife had at last been able to join me and we accepted the Baron's invitation to spend a weekend there.

I wasn't aware, as we drove up the tree-lined road to the moated castle standing out so majestically on the Traunsee, that we would soon find ourselves among members of a defunct European aristocracy whose coronets had toppled in the chaos of war and politics that had engulfed their countries. Many of the aristocrats who converged on Kammerschloss had been prominent leaders in the overrun Balkan kingdoms, and had finally been caught in the throes of acute political crises and the Red Army advance. The world of 1946 was far different from any they had known.

Baron Jesinsky was a most gracious host. We were given a handsome suite of rooms, furnished in superb French antiques.

Dinner was formal. We were shown into a large, high-ceilinged room, its mirrored walls reflecting what seemed like thousands of candles in sparkling crystal sconces. In the center of the room was the largest table I had ever seen. The gleaming silver service was set for thirty guests.

The Duchess Esterhazy, a lovely woman with a quiet, graceful manner, was seated to my left. Occasionally, by the soft candlelight, I detected a sad look in her eyes as we talked. Baron Jesinsky had told me of her enormous past wealth; now the estates and holdings that had been in her family for hundreds of years were in the hands of the Communists. She was a gracious reminder of a world that no longer existed.

"You were able to take nothing with you?" I asked.

"Only these few jewels that we are hopeful can be turned into cash, if one can get a visa to a country where this can be done. Everything else was left behind. But we were fortunate; many refugees brought out nothing at all."

"I'm sorry. Baron Jesinsky told me about the loss of your beautiful home."

The Duchess seemed momentarily lost in memory. My gaze fell upon her hand and I thought these jewels would disappear, one by one, as time slipped by. She caught herself up from her reveries.

"There are worse things than losing one's fortune." She turned to me with her sweet, sad smile. "Enough of this depressing talk." In a time and a place where the saving of life itself was a luxury, the loss of lands and fortunes may seem of minor consequence. Yet, I wondered, if it had happened to me, would I have been as gallant?

After dinner we went into a large paneled room where tables had been set up for cards. The atmosphere was gay with laughter and banter, and had I not known the facts I would have found it difficult to associate these people with recent and possibly continuing personal disaster.

I did not join in the card games and must have been deep in thought for some time before I realized the tone of the evening had changed. The laughter was gone. Hitler's fate was being discussed. Table by table, bridge was forgotten as the discussion became general. This was not a desultory conversation of the day's happenings; the lives of each person in that room had been changed forever by the man of whom they now spoke.

The Czechoslovakian Baron across the room had just remarked that Hitler might still be alive. The Romanian Count sitting near me expostulated, "Ridiculous! He's exactly where the master planner wanted him to be!"

From across the tables came a protest. "One wonders why the master planner would have put him here at all."

"My friend, the master planner in this case was Martin Bormann," the Count answered.

"No," the Czechoslovakian said, "the policies were Hitler's and Hitler's alone. Even Rommel found that out—and to his sorrow."

"That may seem true, particularly in military matters, but no one had more influence in internal matters than Martin Bormann," the Count answered. "He was, without doubt, the cleverest of the Nazis. In the beginning he held a discreet nominal role that kept him close to Hitler. He always appeared dedicated to Hitler; he was never negative, no matter how insurmountable the problem; he applied himself unselfishly to Hitler, and was deeply solicitous toward him. Bormann proved himself indispensable to Adolf Hitler, although he carefully remained buried within the inner workings of the party. Bormann climbed steadily but never publicly. Not once did he even permit the appearance of seeking glory or title or acclaim. He was the seemingly anonymous pillar upon which the Fuehrer could lean. What he gained was power.

"Later, after Hess's defection to England, Bormann took over as deputy of the Fuehrer. Make no mistake about Bormann—he was a powerful factor in the major Nazi decisions and in most of the vilest ones. It was Bormann who developed the Nazi policies for the treatment of the Slavs in the event of German victory over Russia. All Slavs were to be compounded in concentration camps, reduced solely to slave labor for the Germans, given the meagerest food. They were to receive no education; they were to be sterilized; they were to become extinct. Bormann was an advocate of the extermination of the Jews. He was the planner of the youth vigilante groups."

"A shadowy figure, for one who had such influence over Hitler," countered the Czechoslovakian across the room.

Baron Jesinsky, who had been sitting quietly by, said, "Not so much a shadowy figure, as a figure in the shadows. Every effort was made to keep him that way. You know he was never photographed. Bormann's existence was an extraordinary one. A major effort was sustained to keep him unknown by sight to the people within Germany and the world at large. Hitler decreed in 1937, and never retracted the order, that Martin Bormann was not to be photographed under any circumstances. To keep Bormann's identity unknown, the order was reissued periodically."

It was at this point that another guest, with apparent insight or information, expressed a view that seemed an epilogue to the tale told by Carlo.

"In my opinion, every move that Martin Bormann made was carefully planned years before, so that the huge amounts of money put into foreign banks for Hitler's escape might one day be Bormann's. It is also certain that Bormann did not want to see those carefully located millions dissipated in dormant accounts through eternity."

Baron Jesinsky looked to his guest with a startled glance. "What do you know of this?"

"An acquaintance of mine, someone I regard highly, told me the monies are in Switzerland, held in banks under strictest secrecy."

"Well, it's not impossible," Baron Jesinsky said. "There's a severe law in the Swiss banking system that protects the secrecy of the banker and his client."

The Romanian Count added, "If the Swiss banks had not established this form of banking, they would never have become the traditional haven for world-wide capital seeking safety."

"It is as you say," the Baron declared. "Switzerland will always be the perfect depository for this kind of money if it can maintain a stable currency and its historic neutrality." He added, "Conveniently for Hitler, the Swiss Banking Secrecy Act made it a penal offense for anyone working in a Swiss bank to violate any banking confidence."

The Baron now rose and pressed refreshments upon his guests. Several decanters were carried by a servant; the Baron walked along, pouring and serving. The ladies were offered cigars. The only woman smoking cigarettes was my wife.

The Romanian Count had walked over and sat down near me. He seemed interested in the fact that I was the only American man present and it may have been my foreignness that caused him to pursue the subject we had just been discussing.

"We have spoken of Hitler's fortune and of the banking laws in Switzerland, but no one has told you of the elaborate escape system set up by Bormann. There was such a system, and there are those who believe that Bormann, in some manner, saw to it that Hitler committed suicide."

Although no two settings could be more different from one another than this elegant castle and the forested lodge, I found myself trying to merge the tales I had heard at each. Carlo's

38

story, though neither duplicated nor matched in detail by this one, was given some credit from this completely dissociated source. The parallel, uneven as it was, struck me as startling, and challenged my previous attitude concerning Carlo's probable reliability.

Carlo's stories, in retrospect, had seemed bold adventures in fantasy—possibly inspired by some substance in fact, but hugely embellished and heightened by an adept and natural spinner of tales. Perhaps they were no more than that, but I had begun to suspect they might have a forgeable link with reality. I thought that I should like to see Carlo again. I would listen to him with no less interest and with much more care.

6

It was late winter before I had a chance to talk further with Carlo. I had arrived at the lodge alone in the evening and during a thundershower. I waited in my car, hoping the rush of water would ease. After perhaps ten minutes, I gave up the idea of outwaiting the rain and made a dash across the graveled courtyard. I knocked at the huge door and waited. There was no response. Finally I shoved the door open and entered the shadowy hall.

A man was standing by the hearth. As he turned toward me, I recognized Carlo. He was startled by my sudden appearance.

"Ah! It is you! I did not hear anyone because of the rain."

"I knocked, but there was no answer. The door was open. Isn't Erlot here?"

"Everyone has gone to bed—except me. In this storm I guess no one was expected. Come to the fire. Schnapps?"

"Good idea," I replied.

I took off my coat and warmed myself at the hearth as Carlo walked across the room to the decanter and filled two glasses. He returned and handed one to me. He drained his glass and, with a casual gesture toward the cold, rainy night, said, "This storm will stay. Nobody will come out, not even the Gemse!"

"Well, enough rainy days will help to preserve the game," I said.

"No matter, it is plentiful. The mountain goats were brought in from Hungary by Goering. He fancied himself a hunter; his lodge was in the highlands not far from here."

I welcomed the opportunity to draw Carlo out. "Yes, I saw Goering's hunting lodge several weeks ago."

"Did you? It was the fashionable hunting place for the Nazi hierarchy."

"Isn't that where Goering stayed during Hitler's last days in the bunker?"

"Yes, it was from there his unwelcome telegram was sent, when he offered himself to Hitler as the new Fuehrer." Carlo paused a moment, then continued. "Hitler was so infuriated that he ordered Goering's arrest."

"Those last hours must have been indescribable chaos," I said.

Carlo remained silent, seeming lost in thought. As the moments passed and the silence lengthened, Carlo sat almost motionless in the big lounge chair. I wondered if I could not set him off with a question.

"Did Hitler select Admiral Raeder to become his successor?"

"Successor?" Carlo came to life. "Hitler intended no succession; he decreed that everything should die with him—the Third Reich, its leaders, the whole of Germany. If it were possible he would have taken all of the German people with him."

"Was he that mad? But what made Goebbels finally commit suicide too? If he didn't think he could survive in Germany, didn't he at least think of escape?"

"You must understand. Of all the inner circle, Goebbels was Nazism's only real disciple, the only one who was completely, fanatically devoted to Hitler. When he saw his Fuehrer go down, to him that was the end. Besides himself, he sacrificed his wife and his six children on the altar of dying Nazism."

"What about Bormann?"

Carlo shrugged. "Who knows? Bormann was not like the others."

"So I understand," I said. "But if he was the power that I have heard he was, he certainly led Hitler into a bottomless pit. Why wasn't the escape plan used?"

"You do not understand the complete collapse of the man Hitler. While those left around him were hoping desperately that he would flee, he thwarted each suggestion of escape by shouting that the 'tide would turn'; then immediately he would sink into another depression. When he had finally decided to destroy himself, his decision was kept from all but a very select group—Goebbels, Otto Skorzeny—

"And Bormann?"

"Yes, Bormann must have known."

Remembering the conversation at Kammerschloss, I decided to try an approach from another direction. "I was told that incredibly huge funds were accumulated in Swiss banks and that Martin Bormann had access to them. After Hitler's suicide, what happened to all of this money?"

"You ask me questions I cannot answer. What you suggest is, of course, possible." He walked over to the decanter and poured himself another drink. "Yet I have heard that Martin Bormann was killed in the railroad yards outside of Berlin. If that is so, he would have little use for the money now."

He filled his glass again, turned back toward me, and smiled. He walked across the room to his favorite chair and sank into it. "You have become fascinated by the intricate puzzle of the Third Reich. You are intrigued by its strange stories. Would you like me to tell you the strangest of them all? It is a long story, but I promise you it is an exciting one. It will rain tomorrow and there will be no hunting; you can sleep late. So, would you care to sit by the fire and hear an amazing adventure?"

I looked at Carlo, sensing that the accomplished storyteller was about to reveal his favorite tale. All else had been prologue, no more than preparation for this occasion. I looked closely at Carlo. He seemed lazily at ease, his body relaxed in the spaciousness of the large chair. But his eyes were bright.

By way of answer, I rose, placed a heavy log on the fire, and then sat facing him.

PART II

The Hoax

7

For reasons that will appear later in their proper sequence, the "amazing adventure" related to me by Carlo was not written down for a period of some ten years from its first telling. It had, by then, settled into my mind as a story in its own right seen from my perspective, that is, from the Allied point of view.

Aside from that, which is reflected mainly in tone and narrator's sympathy, I have taken as few liberties as possible. I have bridged small gaps in time to give the narrative continuity, and I have amplified, where necessary, the dialogues and descriptions to approximate the essence of Carlo's full narrative.

Carlo told me a well-rounded, richly detailed, and, in the old-fashioned sense, a spellbinding story. In the section that follows, I have tried, as well as memory and translation from two languages into a third permit, to remain faithful to the original.

✠   ✠   ✠

It was an evening early in March 1944. In the countryside around Copenhagen it had been dark for at least two hours. From the ground, an unseen plane could be heard. It flew quick, tight circles, then the engines sputtered. Below, two small lights, taken from the boat lying quietly on the nearby water, were lit. The landing area, dimly marked by the lights, was barely visible from the sky. The plane circled again, then glided in a low sweep, paralleling the ground at about two thousand feet. A man fell away from the plane, his parachute appearing like a puff of black smoke. The drop had been made.

There had been several drops within that general area during the previous four weeks, each calculated for easy, although late, detection by the Nazis. Allied intelligence intended to make it difficult for the Germans to recognize the singular significance of this night's action.

The descending parachutist could see, spread out to the north, the semicircle of Copenhagen and, beyond, the dense gray shape of occupied Denmark. Even in the darkness the country looked flat and wide as it rolled away into the low, far-off horizon. He saw, or imagined he saw, a blink from the bomber's navigational light—a salute to him? The plane had been following an easterly heading; soon, in a wide sweep it had altered course to confuse possible enemy spotters and, only moments later, was circling some miles away to the west.

The parachutist dropped into the neglected and overgrown field that had been purposely selected by Danish resistance forces. The silent, waiting men, who had long since extinguished the dim lamps, ran toward the man and hurriedly gathered up his parachute. Then, without apparent signal, they dispersed. It was difficult to see the elusive shadows as they scattered into the darkness in the vague direction of their boat.

The now-earthbound man turned in the direction of an ancient road that ran north and south. Stumbling through the tall grass, he pushed forward. The only sound, save his own rustling movements, was the endless deep, hoarse croaking of frogs. When he reached a drainage ditch, which he obviously expected to find, he walked along it and quickly, but carefully, drew toward the road.

He located the pickup car by means of a prearranged identification—a small, low-density light. Without hesitation he entered the rear of the vehicle. The car then sped north toward Kastrup airfield. Somewhere along the highway, near Kastrup, the car disappeared into a dark side road.

Twenty minutes later, a German military plane from Madrid, carrying a German major general, arrived at Kastrup airfield. It had hardly come to a stop when one of the crewmen dashed out and across the field to the duty officer, who immediately placed a call for military transportation. A corporal-chauffeur tossed away his cigarette, got into the driver's seat of a limousine, and drove to the military passengers' ramp. He now moved with precision, jumping out, standing at rigid attention as the Major General strode to the car. The heavy luggage was placed in the front seat beside the chauffeur; the Major General continued to carry his own attaché case.

The car moved deliberately through the restricted military area of the airfield, then increased speed down a strip of road, bordered on both sides by the riprap of the breakwater. It rolled up to the drawbridge sentry post, one of the most rigid check points in the occupied countries. The General showed no concern while his several passes and identifying documents were being examined, nor did his driver, who, having delivered the papers to the control post, chatted briefly with one of the guards; the corporal was well known to the men at the check point. Clearance was received with surprising speed. The chauffeur hurriedly returned to the car. He received a curt reprimand from the General for the small delay.

They left the drawbridge behind and started down the blacked-out highway toward Copenhagen. Abruptly, the car turned off the highway into an almost hidden road and stopped.

The chauffeur sat motionless as several men moved briskly through the dark from the edge of the road. The startled Major General leaned forward.

"Was ist los? Was ist los?"

Both rear doors opened almost simultaneously and automatic rifles were thrust into the passenger compartment of the limousine.

The General's voice rose in pitch, partly from anger, partly from fear.

"Was macht! Unmöglich."

The lone occupant of the back seat was ordered out of the car by the chauffeur, who now also held a gun. The General still sat. The corporal's gun approaching his temple brought him out.

He was ordered toward the farmer's truck standing close by. As the group reached it, the Major General made a lunge for the gun of the closest man. Instantly a lanyard whipped around his neck and was jerked tight. Several other shadowy figures merged on the group. One of them said, "We'll take over. You'd better hurry."

The speaker turned and opened the door of the truck. Hanging neatly inside were two German uniforms—those of a major general and his orderly, a lieutenant. The parachutist and one man from the assault party jumped into the truck and closed the door. Several minutes later they emerged in uniform, the parachutist now dressed as a major general, the other as a lieutenant.

They moved toward the car, whose motor the corporal was idling impatiently. He called softly, "Better move, sir!"

As the car sped along the highway, the three uniformed men strained to see the black, onrushing countryside. There was as yet no evidence of the city which the impostor General had seen outlined in the distance during his parachute descent.

"Everything work out okay? Easy drop?" The chauffeur asked.

"Yes. Fine. Any change in plans?"

"None. No trouble. Smoke before you go in?"

"No thanks."

"I can slow down now. I had a few minutes to make up."

"You're fine now. We should be getting close. I think we'll make it just right."

"Let's hope we're just right for everything—all the way!"

It is possible that no men had ever had more intensive training for a mission than these three racing through the night. Yet each man knew the tension compounded of imminent danger, long odds, and the possibility of a drawn-out, indescribably cruel death at the hands of a brutal enemy.

Like the corporal-chauffeur, the lieutenant had been previously planted in Copenhagen, woven into the official German Wehrmacht personnel records as one of the special aides personally chosen by the Major General and always at his disposal. They were known to appear and depart with unexpected suddenness, being under extraordinary orders that permitted enormous freedom of movement.

Now, as they neared the city, they could see the outlines of the buildings, only shades darker than the moonless background. The lieutenant turned to the General.

"There it is. Have you ever been here before?"

"No, never. But I think I know damned near every square inch of it."

As they came into the city, the car slowed and moved through the dark, almost-deserted streets. An occasional pedestrian stared at the big limousine as it passed. The impostor General fingered the medals on his uniform and spoke with a bitterness in his voice.

"I'll bet they hate our Nazi guts!"

"I'd hate like hell to be a German alone with any of them," the corporal said, his words coming forth in effortless German.

As if by a signal no more English was spoken. From this point on, no slightest tolerance could be left to chance. For these three impostors the desperate journey had passed the point of no return.

The limousine pulled up before a handsome hotel. With speed and precision the chauffeur and orderly flanked the door of the limousine and stood at attention as the General stepped out. Carrying only their attaché cases, they entered the hotel lobby, which swarmed with German military personnel. The impostor General strode with conspicuous directness across the marble floor toward the bank of elevators at the far side. The orderly raced ahead to the desk clerk, a German army private, and asked if the General's room was ready. The clerk stiffened to attention as the General passed by, then assured the lieutenant that the suite was ready. The orderly hurried to catch up with the General and the corporal, who were just entering an empty elevator.

As they turned and faced the lobby, a heavy-set, tall officer called out to the Major General.

"We missed you at the war games, your Excellency."

"Yes, and I missed La Roche–Guyon," was the ready reply.

The impostor, as a result of the months of preparation for this assignment, recognized the man who spoke to him as an infantry general from Rommel's staff. Additional data: collected first editions, loved his unfaithful wife, and was troubled with an occasional touch of gout. The masquerader was grateful for the unrelenting long hours spent absorbing the hundreds of pictures of and the minute details concerning the acquaintances of the Major General.

When they entered the elegant, top-floor apartment, there was not the slightest relaxation of their impersonations, even though they were within the General's private suite. They assumed the suite was routinely under surveillance and equipped with concealed listening devices. The orderly immediately called service for bourbon for the General.

Presently, there was a knock on the door; a waiter appeared with a decanter and glasses on a tray. The General poured a glass of bourbon and went into the dressing room. He opened the large wardrobe and almost uttered a long whistle. The vanity of the Major General was eloquently displayed in the imposingly long rows of beautifully tailored uniforms.

He changed from his uniform into casual attire: flannel trousers, a soft shirt with a silk neckerchief, and a velvet smoking jacket. He felt an unexpected relief in being temporarily rid of the several rows of medals, most of which had been bestowed upon the former owner by the Fuehrer himself. Leisurely he walked out to the cold portico balcony off the main living room of the apartment. This had been a habit of the German General's.

He was now alone, this man who—several months later, after the masquerade had been discovered—was to be code-named by Heinrich Himmler for purposes of identification. American or British? Even then the Germans did not know. Therefore, A for American, and B for British, with an added Nazi touch intended as a slur against America—A for "Abraham." They did not know his nationality and never would, but Himmler's classification will suffice—Abraham B. And now, on the first night of his assignment, Abraham B., posing as a German major general, a high-ranking officer of the General Staff and courier for the Fuehrer himself, stood alone in the cold March night air of Copenhagen in occupied Denmark. Would spring come this year? Would he see it?

As he looked out across the city, Abraham B. thought of the strange course of events that had put him here playing so deadly a game.

Precariously holding the hopes of the free world, Allied strategists worked through long days and nights. The awful weight of responsibility for the invasion of Europe lay clearly and heavily upon their shoulders. When the decision was finally reached to invade through Normandy at a beach to become famous under the code name Omaha, rather than the more plausible coast at Calais, the question of diversionary tactics arose. Were there any means to gain advantages for the amphibious Allied landings against the well-trained, hardened, and mobile German land army?

It is not likely we shall ever know just how Allied intelligence came to focus upon one member of Hitler's inner circle, a man so capable that only the most important missions were turned over to him. He was completely trusted by Hitler and, as his private envoy, answered to no one but the Fuehrer. It is equally unlikely that we shall ever know just where and how the scheme for this extraordinary impersonation took shape into a hazardous reality, a gamble considered possible of success, despite the near-incredible odds against it.

Abraham B. met the initial demands for this strange undertaking. He looked like the real General; he also spoke fluent English, German, and French, as did the German Major General.

Did he possess the degree of icy intelligence and discipline that could surmount both the predictable and unpredictable barriers that faced the impersonator? He had to undergo the most rigorous training, the results of which the German investigation later showed. Abraham B. had been worked and tested endlessly, then left to himself for short periods, completely isolated to study, then returned to the merciless, seemingly endless days, weeks, months of training. He had to acquire a new set of habits, maintain a new diet, and hold a precise weight. He had to look like, act like, think like another man— a complex, highly intelligent, and somewhat secretive person. Beneath that polished façade Abraham B. had to acquire still another personality—the espionage agent. Only beneath that did the ordinary man, or perhaps the very extraordinary man, exist.

The real German General was under the most intense surveillance, not only by the Allies, but by the Germans themselves; a few of those watching him were high-ranking members of the German General Staff, officers who wanted to overthrow Hitler and the Nazis and free Germany.

Once the decision to attempt this perilous impersonation had been made, it is not difficult to imagine some of the events that followed: the shock of recognition as Abraham B. saw on the film screen before him an unknown face in his own likeness, and after that, intense examinations by a group of experts from military intelligence, then plastic surgeons, then orthopedists; every line, every structure of bone, was minutely examined.

It was a ruggedly handsome man that Abraham B. studied, a man who carried his tall frame like an athlete, yet with an unusual grace of movement. His carriage was erect and, in spite of a husky build, he moved with agility and quickness. There was an air of decision about him. His dark hair was beginning to streak with gray and his dark eyes had an intense look to them.

Abraham B. studied every movement—learning the particular turn of the head, the tightening of the jaw when the General became annoyed. There was a marked difference in their speech, which had seemed insurmountable for a time. Diction experts had been brought in. The Major General spoke in High German, reflecting his background, but there was a certain colorful turn of words that was almost solely his. When this phase was finally over, the colorful use of words was Abraham B.'s as well. These were the early steps on a long road, completely shrouded in secrecy, that would lead to Copenhagen— and so far beyond that not even the most imaginative member of Allied intelligence could guess its strange turnings.

Abraham B. filled his lungs with the cold night air, expelled it, and went inside.

His immediate task was to unlock the courier's attaché case. He must know the General's current assignments; on his ability to fulfill these without arousing suspicion would depend the initial success of the mission.

There were a few papers in code marked "Madrid"—possibly material the General had picked up en route and was to transmit personally. When his contact arrived, he would turn this over for decoding and for a decision on whether it needed action on his part.

He found a small notebook that contained what seemed to be a list of the General's recent assignments. An entry under

"Madrid" had been marked: "Col. F. called away. Return March 22." There was a final entry, labeled "Copenhagen." He read it and rang for his orderly.

"Call Colonel Steilban," he ordered. "Tell him I have arrived and wish to see him at once."

His first guess about the coded material must have been wrong. Apparently the General expected to return to Madrid with papers that had to be delivered personally to Colonel Fleig. He felt a brief sense of relief; the only remaining assignments in the General's file involved routine interviews with Colonel Steilban and Colonel Fleig. Yet this increased the likelihood that he might soon receive a summons to report to Berlin, or even to Berchtesgaden. Allied intelligence had had to reckon with this possibility, but it was one Abraham B. had no stomach for.

As he was relocking the attaché case, his orderly appeared with the Colonel's card.

"Show him in," Abraham B. said, as he took the card.

The orderly returned with a stocky, broad-faced man. He thrust out his arm. "Heil Hitler!"

"Heil Hitler. What have you to report?" Abraham B. asked with a coldness only short of disdain.

"We've not yet been able to find out the types of amphibious ordnance in the Channel staging area."

"What do you mean you've not yet been able to find out? With a mass build-up like that you *must* know!"

"But, General, we know the shipping has increased. Intelligence is refining the facts."

"The hell with refinement! We must know their amphibious ordnance. Need I warn you and your division of the eventualities if this information isn't forthcoming—and speedily!"

"But, General, you realize England is an island. It is difficult to come and go as we would wish."

"Do not be impertinent; of course I know this. But we must know what our actions are to be."

"Yes, your Excellency. Our surveillance is intense. I expect to have more data at any moment."

"Let's hope so. Contact me either in Stockholm or Paris—Stuelpnagel's office. That's all."

"Heil Hitler!"

"Heil Hitler."

Abraham B. watched the Colonel's half-bow and salute—he observed a swarthy man with close-cropped hair, obviously a good soldier. Then in his curt tone, he added, "Instruct the motor-pool commandant immediately to execute and process orders to transfer the corporal to my personal staff. It is probable that I will keep him with my staff through the next tour."

"Immediately, sir. Heil Hitler."

Abraham B. motioned with his hand and his orderly showed the Colonel to the door.

And so it was over—the first encounter.

Abraham B. sat down in the comfortable club chair. Face to face with the first of those he was to deceive, he had sensed the chasm that divided them. Of the many more he would have to deceive in the clouded future, might not just one, he thought, detect something fraudulent and so bring an end to this grim masquerade?

Allied underground agents shadowed the departing German colonel. They would report back, in case of any unusual move.

After about a quarter of an hour, the special contact, dressed as a German officer, arrived at the suite. He carefully wrote out the subjects they were to discuss, and to allay the suspicions of any who might be listening to the microphones in the room, they talked about the scheduled time of departure from Kastrup airport the following evening and their theoretical safety from attack by American or British fighter planes that might be returning from their scattered squadrons.

Meanwhile, as planned, the two were quickly reviewing the contents of the kidnaped General's attaché case and exchanging brief notes. The agent took the papers that required decoding.

When he realized that the General's assignments had now been almost completed, he shook his head at Abraham B. with a grimace of wry sympathy; he, too, understood the implications.

As soon as their brief interview was over, Abraham B. lit a match to their notes and watched the flames burst and die out. The charred paper curled and crumpled, a last wisp of smoke rose lazily, and, involuntarily, he shuddered.

Snow had fallen intermittently all week. Flakes were falling the next evening when Abraham B. and his two companions drove to Kastrup.

As they passed along the road where the Major General had been captured, they saw nothing more than a shadowed outline of a small farm, partly hidden in the trees.

After a few minutes they reached the heavily guarded drawbridge. Again the careful examination of documents, then they were waved on.

The military plane was warming up its engines as they drove up and boarded. In only a few moments the plane noisily lifted into the dark sky toward Stockholm.

8

The take-off roar of the engines changed to a steady drone. Abraham B. leaned back in his seat and reviewed his position. Within the next few hours, he would be facing one of the most beautiful women in Europe—and the most treacherous phase of his mission. Once again he reviewed the facts he knew so well.

The Major General and the Countess had met at a hospital benefit in Berlin in 1934. The Countess had just returned from Connecticut, a sought-after young widow whose marriage to a wealthy American had ended in tragedy. That meeting between the lovely Countess and the striking General flowered into romance, but gradually cooled for her sometime after he became adjutant to the Fuehrer. For the next few years the Countess remained aloof, but for the past year she had become his companion once more. Their relationship had not resumed its early fervor; they were friends, literally—no longer lovers. A graceful companionship, something from an outmoded, almost antique way of life, seemed all either of them wished.

During the intervening years she had moved through the capitals of the world, a restless spirit in quest of something she was unable to find. There had been a succession of lovers, none of whom she regarded seriously or for long. Now she seemed to have wearied of games of the flesh.

Abraham B. had been carefully indoctrinated. The Allied planners were counting heavily on the present lack of intimacy between the Countess and the General; it permitted a deception that their earlier relationship would have made too hazardous, almost certain of failure. The salon allowed a remoteness that the bedchamber did not. Yet the Countess was a tempting challenge for any man. Abraham B. must be prepared for any change; he had to face the possibility that the Countess, if she even suspected the deception, would have to be disposed of, permanently and quickly. Miles of tape of some of her most intimate conversations had been run for him. In his mind she remained a whore—a very glamorous one.

The Countess had become an agent of the Abwehr, the German intelligence service, until it was dissolved by Hitler's order in February 1944, after the Gestapo exposé of the Kiep network. She was then sent to Stockholm in the employ of Himmler's R.S.H.A., the newly created master intelligence service. There she maintained a luxurious apartment and a handsome farm retreat.

Abraham B. thought ruefully that, aside from her beauty, she had only one saving grace; she had shown some discernment in her indifference to Hitler. He had invited her to his opulent galas at the Fuehrerhaus in Munich. She had attended many yet somehow avoided the more frequent small intimate parties. The Countess apparently had not wanted to be locked within the insane trappings of Hitler's world. She knew that at best the Fuehrer's reputation with women was veiled; that the evenings Hitler most fondly cherished, known within the Abwehr's higher circles, were those in which there would be a group of admiring young women gathered closely around him. He always boasted of his moral conduct, yet his niece, who had been very close to him, died a violent death at the age of twenty-three, officially reported a suicide by the police. Could Eva Braun have been put aside for the Countess? No one will know, but it was thought that Hitler had never quite forgiven the Countess for her tacit rebuff of him.

When their plane arrived in Stockholm, a chilling wind swept from the black sky. A heavy fog lay over the airport making hazy halos of the lights.

As they drove into the city, they passed along the waterways of Stockholm. The frozen lakes and the promenades were covered with moving designs of warmly dressed skaters: families, school groups, lovers, young, middle-aged, elderly. Those not skating lingered about the banks, casually celebrating their joy of living. It was a beautiful sight, happy in contrast to the hell of war and waste beyond this neutral land.

Abraham B., the lieutenant, and the corporal rode slowly through Stockholm. Throngs of people cluttered the sidewalks and the pedestrian crossings of the streets. They moved briskly as the chilling wind from the northeast rolled the night fog along.

Abraham B. thought of the other major cities of the Continent: Nazi-throttled Paris; London, free but hit continually by the deadly blitz; Rome, now occupied by its former partner; and Berlin, citadel of evil. What a blessed people were the free Swedes!

The car arrived at the General's apartment-hotel. The three were well aware of unknown danger about them; German S.S. and S.D. security men were thick throughout Stockholm. They entered the lobby of the hotel, moving with feigned ease through the well-appointed and beautiful interior. It was time for Abraham B. to telephone the Countess. She never knew the General's exact time of arrival; his itinerary was kept from her. But it had been his habit to call soon after he arrived to let her know he was in Stockholm. This time there was no need to send flowers in advance of his arrival because her favorite "bit of heliotrope" was out of season and unobtainable as far north as Sweden. The call was answered by a maid who told him the Countess was expected very soon. He replied that he would shortly leave his hotel for the Countess' apartment.

They left the hotel in the Rolls-Royce that the corporal

ordered from the hotel garage and drove along the streets at a smooth, comfortable speed. Abraham B. was soon to be beyond his partners' aid. Sitting back, he relaxed and held a cigarette which his orderly obediently lighted for him. They carried out their roles as if under intense scrutiny.

The limousine made its way into the central part of the city and quietly rolled to a stop in front of an immense apartment building with a massive stone facing. An impressive sight, it stood like a maze of towers, formidable against the dark, fog-veiled sky.

Abraham B. felt an intense loneliness as he walked toward the entrance. He passed through the entrance hall into a grand lobby. His nerves tensed as he walked toward the elevator which was to take him to the top floor where the Countess maintained her suite.

He shared the elevator with a young Swedish couple, and felt their indignation toward him, a German. Their utter scorn fell upon him like a shadow, as he stood in his elaborate uniform. When they left the elevator, he felt a strong urge to go out after them and explain who he really was. He smiled wryly, knowing they would think him mad as well as demonic.

And then he found himself before the door of the Countess' apartment. He pressed the bell button.

The door of the apartment was quietly opened by a neat maid. Her hair was carefully braided in a typically German style; her simple uniform was severe, impeccable.

Abraham B. allowed himself a perfunctory, curt greeting and walked past the maid into a small sitting room outfitted with cigarettes, ash trays, and a few books—each in German and extolling the glorious Nazi state. He seemed relaxed as he waited quietly, fingering the limited book offerings. He had just picked up one of the books when he heard a soft, surprisingly appealing voice. The Countess had entered. Facing her, he clicked his heels, bowed, and kissed her extended hand.

He was looking at one of the loveliest women he had ever

seen. As they moved through the room, he studied her as the real General—indeed, as any man—might; he noted her hair done into a graceful chignon to one side of her head, the long, gently arched line of her throat, the flawless skin visible between the curves of her slightly tanned breasts. He sensed as he looked into her eyes something of a visual, soft caress.

This was a charm he had never before encountered. He knew the real German General had once been enticed by these most subtle gestures. And this was the enemy. Little wonder that she had kept the General fascinated over the years. Abraham B. felt a kind of sympathy for him; this was a loveliness that could easily insist upon possession, possession that, denied, could mean torment. The poor devil.

They sat in the large, beautifully appointed salon. She had, as always, the ingredients of a Martini readied. He felt he had to turn away from her, but was irresistibly drawn back and caught unexpectedly in her face a tinge of enmity, a sudden animosity which she covered so quickly with a smile he was not sure he had seen it. Had he committed some blundering gesture to bring this flicker of change in her? She offered him the Martini she had poured, then raised her glass. They touched glasses. Again he felt the unexpected attraction. He forced himself to remember the true nature of this woman beside him.

She raised an arm and let her hand cushion her soft, brown hair. He realized how gracefully she moved, even in so casual a gesture; or was every movement studied? She smiled and said, "So. You have been playing at your war games, General—and neglecting me."

"The last thing I would have chosen."

He reached for her hand, but she, as if anticipating him, moved forward to pick up a silver box.

"Cigarette? I think that you will find your brand."

He declined and, after a moment, she stood up.

"I wish to go out to dine tonight."

"Then we will, of course. You're very beautiful," he told her.

* * *

At the restaurant the proprietor greeted them effusively, then led them forward. Abraham B. searched the data file of his mind; was the General well known here? Yes, he must be. As they walked through the room he allowed the ghost of a smile to appear on his face, an imperious acknowledgment of greeting should his eyes meet a glance that implied recognition.

When they were seated and had ordered, the Countess turned to Abraham B. and said, "What news of home? The Swedes feel we will be beaten."

"The Swedes! What do they know of modern war! You must learn patience. Rommel has said—"

"Please, I am sorry I asked. For this evening, can we not forget the war?" There was a pause, then she said, "I seem to have displeased the Fuehrer. It's been many months since I have received an invitation from him."

"You haven't displeased him—he is simply not entertaining these days. A precaution to protect him from the fanatics who would destroy him."

"Violence is the fear of rulers of violence, is it not? This horrible war; I wish someone would end it!"

"My dear, please! You might be overheard and misunderstood. You must be more careful of what you say. It is known that you were married to an American."

Her sudden light laugh was infectious. He found it difficult to match her quicksilver shifts in mood.

"Oh my dear—don't be so fearful. The Fuehrer certainly has no such reservations toward me!"

"There are few who are not suspected by Himmler."

"Are you suspected?" she asked teasingly.

"Of course not! But there is only a handful of us who are still trusted."

He welcomed the arrival of their dinners and made the most of that diversion. He determined that for the remainder of the evening he would play at being the courtly admirer, avoiding any discussion more serious than her obvious loveliness.

For a week Abraham B. paid court to the Countess. The remoteness of the first meeting diminished. Now he found her to be a happy audience for his performance. The days in Stockholm sped by.

Under her veneer of sophistication, were there redeeming qualities? If she had been born in another place at another time, might not she have been—?

He caught himself. This kind of thinking could bring him to the verge of complete disaster.

Abraham B. met regularly with his contact; daily progress reports were filtered back to Allied headquarters. The plan, in its initial phase, had to remain flexible although its purpose remained fixed. Abraham B. knew that the decision to proceed would be determined not only by the successful deployment of his espionage team, but by the demands of a much larger plan of which his mission was a part.

The real General would be spending much time with the Countess; Abraham B. followed that pattern. He was searching for the slightest sign that would suggest she suspected the deception. The Countess was under the most intense surveillance by Allied agents; so, too, were other known members of the German intelligence network. By the end of a week it appeared that Abraham B. was completely accepted in his role.

On his eighth day in Stockholm, Abraham B. received word that the plan was to move into its second phase. This put into effect several carefully calculated actions.

A German agent in London, who had long since defected to the Allies, had been fed occasional pieces of accurate information that he, in turn, transmitted to Berlin. Now he sent word that he had gained access to classified material of extreme secrecy and importance. He had previously passed documents to the real General in Madrid; these encounters had been carried out without the slightest flaw. As expected, Berlin instructed that the same procedure now be followed.

Abraham B., in a routine manner, had indicated to Berlin

that his plans called for an imminent return to Madrid. He, too, received orders from Berlin to meet the agent; he was further directed to gain an initial evaluation from the highest military authority immediately concerned. This was one of the several alternatives that had been foreseen by the Allied planners.

Abraham B. realized that the hazards of his mission would be multiplied once that document was in his hands. He knew as well that countless lives might then depend on how well he and his partners played out their drama. Soon there would be no turning back, no possibility of reprieve.

It was with this mounting sense of anticipation and fear that he accepted the Countess' invitation to go to her country house the day before he was to leave for Madrid.

9

As they left the outskirts of Stockholm, Abraham B.'s spirit was quickened by the bright morning sun that highlighted the maze of sparkling channels between the sand bars. He could hear the murmur of the swift wind from aloft and see its strength as it combed the marsh grass from the sea along its path.

They passed occasional cyclists who had the weathered look of the sea. As the car rambled through the sandy country, crossed a rise of land, and passed down a long stretch of sun-dappled dunes and channels, they saw at a distance brightly colored, wind-filled sails. A small, open tidal basin was jammed with the striped, multicolored spinnakers of small craft, filled by the sea winds. Closer, they could make out the shapely hulls listing and skimming ahead of the wind. Abraham B. looked at the Countess, who was driving. She turned and, for a long moment, their eyes held.

When they arrived he noted well-trimmed larch hedges fencing the farm's extended reaches. The fields fell away like endless lawns, green and smooth. Occasional stretches were furrowed brown. He reached for the Countess' hand and held it as they walked the long distance to the main house. Her glance was at first questioning, then she smiled at him. They seemed in tune with the peace and beauty about them. To the east stood a cluster of large trees and the battlements of an ancient castle, long left to the weather and the green-brown patina of nature. It contrasted sharply with the rest of the well-kept farm. He stopped to admire it.

"How beautifully nature undoes the works of man!"

He turned to the Countess to share this scene with her only to find a look of astonishment on her face. He realized he had spoken without thinking for the first time since he had known her. He cursed himself silently as he remembered: the General could not tolerate anything that wasn't precise and well cared for. He added quickly with a smile, "But not so close to the main house, my dear. Can't someone clean this?"

The Countess shrugged, the moment fled, and they continued toward the house. Here and there a scallop shell crunched under their feet. She told him about the castle and how it had been built to fight off the marauding pirates of the twelfth century. He continued to hold her hand as they walked slowly toward the tile-roofed house.

It seemed entirely possible that the Countess had already had occasion to tell the General about the ancient battles. Abraham B. wondered if she was being merely repetitious; he had no way of knowing whether his single blunder would be the fatal mistake. He could only go on as though nothing had happened.

"Those battlements seem peaceful enough now."

She smiled at him. "I hope I can acquire a bit of that peace in my last years."

Nothing more was said as they walked along. Each seemed locked in thought. He saw the topmasts of a schooner, sheltered and moored not far away, just before he opened the door and they entered the house.

There was a pleasant fire burning in the wide hearth. They sat before it, quietly talking of unimportant things, at times not talking at all, and a feeling of intimacy crept into the room as time stole by.

Quite apart from logic, from training, Abraham B. found this association with the Countess running against his grain. He sensed that he might be made to suffer from it. His mind kept avoiding the facts, the evidence, of the Countess' life. Was she, he wondered, as much a masquerader as himself? What did he really know about her? Dangerous thinking, he realized. It was fortunate that he would be leaving the next day for Madrid.

She tossed her sweater on a chair and walked to the fireplace. Abraham B. sat studying her. There was a surprising gentleness in her face. She turned toward him for a moment, the play of firelight accenting her loveliness. For the first time he thought of her as vulnerable. She seemed now a fusion of woman and girl. Gone, so it appeared, was the sophisticated, worldly, unapproachable creature.

"You're very quiet," he said.

"I feel the need for quiet. So many years of noise and confusion—so much unrest." She turned back and looked into the fire for a long moment. "I've never known a lovelier day than this. Today I can almost believe the world is wonderful."

"The world is wonderful. People can make it seem monstrous sometimes."

"I'm afraid I've become one of those people. I don't care very much for my life.

"Then why not change it? You could, you know."

"I'm not so certain."

She seemed thoughtful and preoccupied.

She turned back to the fire, and, after a long silence, said, "I have been thinking of Vienna."

"I miss it, too."

"I didn't mean that. I'm thinking of the days we had together, so long ago. Do you remember?"

"I've never forgotten, but I've thought that you wanted to."

"I thought so, too. Did you know how deeply I loved you then?"

"I've always wanted to believe that you did. What happened to destroy that?"

"You changed." His mind was almost paralyzed when he

heard her next statement. "You've changed again. You are not the same man, my General. You have been three men—each one quite distinct. I think I like this one the best."

He sat stunned, unable to speak. He tried to allay his building fears with the knowledge that she had been referring to the General. He looked into her eyes, searching for some clue, anything to ward off the conclusion his being raced toward. The enmity and resistance, which he had recognized just a few days before, had vanished from her completely.

His training had been thorough, he should have been prepared for this. Yet, somehow, he knew that he wasn't. This time, this place, this woman, all had taken a strong hold on his existence. He was infatuated.

10

A breeze was blowing over the crusted, brown-loam earth of the Spanish Basque country. Masses of green, recently sprung up, dotted the ground. Heavy rainfall had run down the deep, rocky barrancas to the heaving Atlantic. The open country in Spain would welcome more rain which, from the look of the pale graying sky, would soon come.

The car carrying the impostor General and his two companions from Madrid was headed toward San Sebastián on the Bay of Biscay. As they approached varying bends and grades, the road signs read "Curva Peligrosa." They drove through the soft green countryside with its brown undertones; passed a slow, heavily laden oxcart on the road, guided on foot by a solemn, mute Basque wearing the traditional black beret. Here and there they could see flocks of sheep, each with its lone shepherd. Twice they encountered a priest on a bicycle.

Anyone passing through this northern province would admire the beauty of its bleak coast along an ocean of deepest ultramarine. The profile of formidable cliffs ran down into curved beaches, then off into mist. Inland could be seen an occasional church set high on the rocky heights by patient forefathers long gone from the land.

A lonely, strong sea-country, the Basque region, with hardy, good people. Now and again the three Allied agents saw gateways of sturdy dolomite stone, which led into rugged villas and low-lying chalet-type houses. Evidence of an earlier elegance, they had the touch of an archaic simplicity.

In the outskirts of San Sebastián the car was stopped several times before herds of young bulls crossing the road, attended by herdsmen with the slingshots used to guide them. Now they came upon a small, straggly procession led by a burro with a tall rider seated well back, his blanket held across his face to ward off the cold of the spring day, his long thin legs hanging down almost to the ground. The tiny, sure-footed burro that followed was piled high with heavy bracken from the highlands; then came chunky, mud-spattered oxen, wearing tasseled sheepskin caps, pulling multicolored carts laden to the sky. A clattering cavalcade out of Cervantes.

They entered San Sebastián, once the scene of King Alfonso's royal bullfight festivals. Now and then, as from out of the past, a young voice was heard singing a tremulous saeta to the Virgin. In the past, each year the purple veil had been gracefully drawn in the cathedral, and followed, at the moment when the veil was set aside, by a trumpet fanfare of joy. Then there was dancing, with castanets clicking fast rhythms and bells far and near pealing wildly in honor of the risen Christ. The Easter bullfight, with its vivid colors and its jasmine, roses, and carnations, had been the crowning event in the magic week of merriment following the mourning period that retold the agony of the Cross.

The three silent riders drove past the plaza de toros, now empty and quiet. The day of the royal bullfight was over now. No faintest breeze of this romantic past stirred to touch the three men who sped along the winding road. In Madrid, after weighing the course of the deception through Copenhagen and Stockholm, they had reached the decision—proceed to the critical phase of the mission.

Now they headed into German-occupied France, bearing the document for the hoax. For these three the sunlit cliffs of Spain reflected menace. Perhaps they drew solace and courage from the knowledge that the cliffs of Dover would shine brighter and more menacing to the Germans one day soon.

11

Very late in the afternoon the limousine, a large black Mercedes, approached the French frontier at Irún. As they drew near, Abraham B. and his companions saw several swarthy Spanish police stationed on the west side of the international bridge. Across it the French gendarmes, in their short blue coats and round visored hats, moved under the watchful gaze of German soldiers.

The Spaniards, as well as the French and Germans, had been advised of the limousine that would approach the border. They flagged it across with great respect and with no delay whatever. The car touched the French side just as evening came on.

Abraham B. now assumed more punctiliously the mannerisms and bearing of the Major General; the presence of the German army of occupation enhanced the possibility that he might encounter someone who knew the General well.

The road from Irún followed the French coast as it curved toward Biarritz, where they had been instructed to stop and spend the night before going on to Paris. This was the pattern of the Major General whenever he followed this route. Approaching their hotel, they could see the silvery coastline with huge chunks of rocks rising out of the surf into the blackness of the night. The water looked polished as agate; the air was deliciously cold.

The Mercedes stopped before the hotel. Abraham B. imagined how brilliantly lighted the veranda must have been before the war. The orderly hurried around and opened the door, then

Abraham B. stepped out of the car and walked to the hotel entrance. He carried his attaché case.

He dined alone later in the grandeur of a vast old French suite. The only sound was the unceasing distant roll of the ocean. The tall windows were entirely draped for blackout. He had observed that the terrace beyond overlooked the Bay of Biscay; now he rose, turned out the lamps within the room, then opened the large windows and went out into the night. He was hardly aware of the moonlight on the surf to his right. A mood of apprehension settled over him; he could not shake the thoughts of the unknown hazards that lay ahead.

He had been there for only a few minutes when his orderly approached to tell him, in precise military fashion, that the phone operator had asked if the General were receiving phone calls. In surprise, Abraham B. turned and walked into the dark study, now lit only by moonlight. He walked across the room and picked up the telephone. His eyes narrowed, looked straight ahead, as his hand tightened around the receiver.

He was suddenly lifted from his lonely, melancholy thoughts. The soft voice of the Countess told him that she was in the hotel and in a few moments, if he wished, would be on her way to see him.

A sense of caution flooded him. It was certain that his suite was wired, carrying his voice to some listening post within the building. This was the first stop since the final commitment of the mission. The unexpected call—a trap?

He realized at once that he had no choice but to risk it. Without pause, he called to his orderly, his voice echoing like a formidable rumble; it was the voice of the German Major General he imitated so expertly. With a signal to warn of possible danger, he informed his orderly that the Countess was on her way. The chauffeur and the orderly withdrew to the servant's pantry and waited. Action might have to be taken.

As Abraham B. stood there quietly, the darkness began to weigh upon him. He drew some comfort from the shaft of moonlight that shone obliquely in through the window. Again, the only audible sound was the pounding, steady surf. Abraham B. frowned. Why was she here at this time? He had not given her any details of his itinerary. Again he speculated on the chances of a trap. Had he betrayed himself to her? For whom was she acting—herself, or an arm of the Nazi machine? He knew he should fear this unexpected meeting, yet he recognized a sense of elation at the thought of her coming.

He heard the light knock on the door. The orderly moved into the room quickly, signaling to Abraham B. with his arm. Abraham B. turned to the window and pulled the huge drape across the shaft of moonlight.

As the orderly opened the door, Abraham B. could see only a silhouette; the Countess appeared like a dark image against the lighter background. She stood still for a moment, surprised by the dark room, then passed through the doorway into the suite. The orderly nodded, closed the door, and quickly left. Abraham B. again pulled the drape back; the moonlight threw its shafts of slanting light into the room, tracing shadows on the folds of the Countess' gown, revealing the fur draped upon her shoulders.

He looked intently through the dim light of the moonlit room. She appeared before him, her face lovely, soft, but unsmiling. How easy, he thought, to love such a face. The Countess came close to him, so close that he could have reached out and touched her. Her expression had not changed. He could not escape what he saw, and fought to resist the confusion that her enchantment cast about him.

"If I had had three wishes, your being here would have been the first," he told her.

The Countess said nothing but tilted her head slightly, looking up at him. Her eyes told him soundlessly all he could wish to hear. She cast off her fur cape, then sat on the cushioned seat, leaning gracefully forward. Her skin was pale in the moonlight.

He had wondered during the past week whether he would

ever see her again. Now she was before him. He was hardly certain how the real General would behave under these circumstances, even less certain of what was expected of an Allied agent. Only his personal feelings were entirely clear, and he thought ruefully that he wished they weren't. She appeared even more beautiful than Abraham B. remembered as she sat there, quietly looking up at him. He took delight in what he saw— her rich, dark hair, unadorned and needing nothing, her pale face, her dark eyes.

He wished at this moment he knew none of the facts of her file at British intelligence. How different things might be for him, if only, if only— But he did know the facts.

He sat down beside her, conscious that their words would be heard by others.

"How wonderful that we meet," he said.

"Yes, I too think it is wonderful."

"In Stockholm, you said you were going to Berlin, then Paris. I did not expect to see you so soon again. How long are you staying?" he asked.

"As long as I usually stay."

He avoided probing further; this was a blank area in his training. He had no idea how long she had stayed at Biarritz in the past.

She quietly turned and wrote several words on a note pad close by, then handed it to him. She had written that she had come to Biarritz to await his arrival in France. She looked at him strangely and wrote two more words, "Paris office." Abraham B. read the note and nodded knowingly. He wondered to himself what "Paris office" meant.

"And how long will you stay here?" she asked.

"I must leave tomorrow."

"I am sorry you cannot stay a little longer."

He knew this did not reflect the feeling that had existed between the General and the Countess. She looked at Abraham B. with sudden gravity, with a strained hesitation in the lines of her face, an attitude she clearly did not want detected by the unseen listeners. She raised her face to him, her eyes full of meaning.

"I am going to be with you—will you have me?"

Abraham B. might have rationalized his action through several logical arguments, but at this moment he had no choice. Nor would be have acted differently if a choice had been possible. He gazed at the Countess for a long moment, then moved his mouth toward hers. Their bodies drew close and then blended together.

12

A wild unexpected storm roared in across the coastline, pummeling the waves upon the shore. Abraham B. sat in front of the fire. It was five o'clock in the morning, but the overcast sky screened out the dawn. In the eerie half-light the three men listened to the gale outside.

The orderly sat in the closet, the area in the suite least likely to be wired and most removed from the sounds of the storm. He crouched before a portable short-wave receiver, an earphone strapped about his head. Occasionally he exchanged a look with the other two. The chauffeur, tending the small antenna, kept it in slow movement, trying to pick up the expected transmission scheduled for them.

There was complete silence. For the next five minutes, the antenna moved in a slow, continuous pattern. Then the orderly signaled that he was receiving.

The transmission continued for several minutes, repeating the identical message. "Please sail—the wind is rising—thumbs.—Please sail—the wind is rising—" On and on the transmission continued.

As they drove from the hotel, reassured by the radio message, the blackness of the early morning sky broke into a deluge of rain. For a time they pushed forward to the counterpoint of the falling rain and the car's tires slushing along the roadway. As they sped on, a little valley opened before them, and for a moment the sky lightened and the valley seemed to fill with morning light. Then the rain returned.

Abraham B. studied the sky. The weather was very much in their favor. Traveling during daylight hours in open country could be sheer suicide; today, however, the foul weather would protect the roads from Allied fighter planes.

The hum of the car, the soft tattoo of the rain, and the somberness of the countryside began to press in upon Abraham B. His inward brooding possessed him; he could not suppress the now grim thought that he might never again see the Countess. He leaned suddenly forward.

"What the hell—"

The orderly had seen it, too. "I can't tell yet, but it looks like a German convoy."

Abraham B. had recognized the gray cavalcade of war vehicles at the same moment. He touched the chauffeur on the shoulder. "Just take it easy."

"They've stopped," the orderly said. "One of the men is getting out!"

"He has field glasses on us. Show no concern," Abraham B. said, sitting back.

He felt nervous. He glanced at the ambassadorial ensign on their left fender, then at the German General Staff's ensign on the right. He remained well back in his seat as they slowly approached the halted convoy. Abraham B. ceremonially saluted the convoy, returning the salutes he received. They continued to drive by slowly.

For the moment the rain had nearly stopped. The high-ranking officer of the convoy, a general whose eyes in spite of the weather were obscured by dark glasses, and who wore the usual black-and-silver insignia against the green of the Wehrmacht, was ominous looking. He peered intently at the limousine as it passed. His stare seemed overly intense to Abraham B.; it seemed more than mere curiosity. Abraham B. felt a sense of imminent danger building within him.

They had passed two command cars and two troop trucks of the convoy, when they heard the order to halt.

"Stop!" said Abraham B.

He turned his head toward the command car now several paces behind them.

The general in the dark glasses was talking earnestly to one of his staff who was standing in the vehicle, looking down at him. To the three in the limousine, the wait seemed endless. They were quite literally caught in the middle of the convoy. The officer who had been standing in the command car turned and, as one of the German soldiers opened the door, he stepped down onto the roadway and walked directly toward them. As the German drew near they could see that he was a colonel of infantry.

He saluted courteously and with a slight bow said, "Your Excellency, we have just received radio communication that there have been several enemy fighter-plane sweeps made this side of the Orléans district."

"Thank you. I'm glad the weather is no better. How is it ahead?"

"Our radio reports it is getting progressively stormier."

"Good. We must proceed. We will risk it. Thank you, Colonel."

"Your Excellency!" Saluting, he added, "Heil Hitler!"

"Heil Hitler."

The Allied team sped on through the early morning hours, headed toward Orléans where they planned to spend the night before proceeding to Paris the next morning.

13

They had just left Tours on the road to Orléans, paralleling the Loire River. The sky ahead of them was a huge, gray mass. As the road curved wide, they descended upon the town of Blois. It would have been relaxing, under any other circumstances, to stop in Blois at an inn, but they had precise instructions to make no unnecessary stops. They continued on with the rain beating against their windshield.

With the town a mile or so behind they saw a military roadblock. The chauffeur reduced his speed as they neared the check point. Abraham B. attempted to measure the situation from the details of the scene. His eye noted the two old houses near the road, only their front walls left standing. At the farthest corner of the ruins a number of German vehicles were clustered. This was no impromptu block. Just ahead stood two helmeted soldiers with submachine guns; the Mercedes came to a reluctant stop as the nearest soldier raised his arm.

Before them was a large bus, overloaded with people, including several small children. Some three hundred yards ahead, an ox-drawn cart coming from the opposite direction had also been stopped.

The soldier who had motioned them to halt did not take his eyes off them. Any roadblock provided a threat. What a plum, Abraham B. thought, for a German soldier—to bring into custody a high-priority Allied espionage team.

The French faces in the bus, which had now been backed up alongside, bore the stamp of fear and deprivation. The people were ill-dressed; some held small bundles or worn suitcases.

One of the children was crying bitterly. The silent adults appeared to be suffering from hunger and cold. Any traveler happening upon this scene would instantly recognize that misery prevailed on this bit of the earth.

The ox-drawn cart was permitted to proceed through the check point. As it drew closer, the three in the limousine could see that the men who were riding on it looked as though they might be disabled French veterans.

Now an officer approached the car; behind him was a formidable group of heavily armed soldiers. He motioned to a second officer, stopped, and they talked together for a minute. Again they walked forward; one shouted out an order to the chauffeur to pull over to the side of the road.

The chauffeur said softly, "I think this is it!"

The sudden sound of shattering glass seemed to freeze all motion save one. A young Frenchman, hardly more than a boy, had lunged through the window of the bus and was running through a small grove of beech trees beside the road. Just as he reached the river, the machine guns opened up. Suddenly it was over. Abraham B. could not take his eyes off the water. On its surface, a patch of the Loire River ran crimson for just a moment. "Sons of bitches!" he thought. "Foul sons of bitches!"

"Forward!" rang out the order to the chauffeur. The car moved ahead and halted. The officer in charge, a captain, came up, pleased to have had a high-ranking officer as a witness.

"My apologies for the delay, your Excellency. May I see your identification, please?"

Abraham B. was too enraged to speak. He looked away with what he hoped appeared disinterest. The orderly passed the papers out to the captain who, after making a few notes, handed them back.

"These stupid French! They will not learn. As you leave Orléans, please be advised to take the road to the left, the Orléans-Étampes road to Paris. The Fontainebleau road is being used for heavy troop movements."

* * *

All during that long night in Orléans, troop convoys passed constantly. Abraham B. and his team got little sleep. They left Orléans long before daybreak, their apprehension from the previous day somewhat abated.

The early morning was cold and gray. They passed several companies of German soldiers, also en route to Paris. After Angerville, the rain started anew. As they approached Étampes, the road became muddy, in some places dangerous. They began to see a few church spires as they neared the town and the chauffeur decreased speed.

They had just cleared Étampes, placing them twenty miles outside of Paris, when the orderly said, "Look back! I think that gray car could be following us."

Abraham B. turned. The rain had slackened and their visibility was now fairly good. He continued his watch for the next several minutes. Abraham B. suggested that they decrease speed. As they slowed, the gray car behind seemed to gain on them momentarily, then it fell back to its former distance behind.

They continued at a steady pace for about six miles, reduced speed through the village of Arpajon, and, once again in a rural area, quickly increased their speed. Within a few minutes, they again noticed the gray car pacing them.

Abraham B. suggested another maneuver: stop beside the road on the pretext of checking the motor.

The chauffeur pulled over and got out. Abraham B. watched in the rear mirror as the gray car came along the bend of a curve some distance behind. It had barely come into view when it stopped, backed up, and faded from sight around the curve.

After about ten minutes, the chauffeur got back into the car and they drove on. Soon the gray car appeared again in the mirror. No doubt lingered; they were being followed.

After they had entered the outskirts of Paris, they noted that the tail car had closed its distance and was almost upon them. They followed a predetermined route into the city, and soon were well into the southeast district. It was just after eight in the morning when they crossed the Pont Neuf. The river banks were thronged, the city seemed busy.

They continued their journey in the direction of the Place de la Concorde. Beyond, on the gray morning horizon, was the Arc de Triomphe. Despite the crowds, the cyclists, and carts, the gray car stayed close behind them.

"Head for the apartment," Abraham B. said.

They passed into the broad line of one of the boulevards that circles the center of Paris, then turned toward the General's apartment. The car had to come to a traffic stop before what seemed to be an endless mass of bicyclists, and at that point the gray sedan drew to within yards of them for the first time.

The orderly, turning as if to speak to the General, kept unobserved watch on the gray sedan. The chauffeur used his rearview mirror.

It was the chauffeur who spoke first. "There are now two men in plain clothes. The third got out a second ago, when they stopped for traffic."

Traffic moved on again. The chauffeur threaded his way expertly, with what seemed unlimited knowledge of Parisian streets. The limousine turned into a smaller street with less traffic. The gray sedan did not follow. All they could see looming behind them were the faint traces of the towers of Notre Dame, almost invisible in the heavy dark morning sky.

They drew up before a large apartment-hotel reserved for German officers; it stood within a group of fashionable buildings, not far from the center of the city.

About one hundred feet from where they had parked they noticed the gray sedan. There was nothing to do but play their hand with an air of complete calm.

Abraham B. and the orderly entered the building; the chauffeur remained with the car to dispatch the luggage and, if possible, to learn something more about the gray sedan.

In the lobby the orderly announced the General to the desk

clerk. Almost at once two German privates appeared and were sent after the luggage. Abraham B. and the orderly talked for a few moments; they did not want to lose sight of their luggage.

The orderly also inquired about messages for the General. Abraham B. strained his ears to hear the answer. If he were ordered to return to Berlin or Berchtesgaden at once, this was where he would learn of it. There were no messages.

One of the young soldiers reappeared, staggering under four large leather suitcases. The other followed, burdened with three more.

As Abraham B. entered the passenger elevator with the orderly, the chauffeur accompanied by the two soldiers and the luggage was entering the service elevator. Another young German private appeared at the elevator and joined the desk clerk in saluting Abraham B. The desk clerk said, "A pleasure to have you back, your Excellency."

Abraham B. half-saluted in return and said, "Heil Hitler, Heil Hitler."

With that the two Germans jumped to attention. "Heil Hitler, your Excellency! Heil Hitler!"

The suite was huge and elegant. On the marble-topped period dresser in the bedroom was a picture of the Countess in a large silver frame. He walked over to the dresser and removed his visored hat and gloves, admiring the photograph before him.

It was a little past nine in the morning when Abraham B. asked his orderly to draw his bath and unpack his suitcases. The room clerk had dispatched a valet, who had been waiting in the hall to rush the General's uniforms to the press shop and take care of his laundry. The orderly had carefully removed the General's medals and emptied the pockets. It was obvious that the German generals spared themselves no luxury. Soft music echoed through the suite. The bathroom glittered with silver taps and bathing accessories. The beds looked like enormous square, pillowed sofas. The long, mirrored dressing room was filled with uniforms. Closets were lined with boots and shoes of

14

Abraham B. spent a restless night; he dreaded the meeting with Stuelpnagel. He had rehearsed it a thousand times during the training period and he rehearsed it a dozen more during the long night. But how does one rehearse the unexpected? Stuelpnagel was astute. Would it be possible to fool that general? And he was only the first. Rundstedt would soon follow, if everything went according to plan. If he were a statistician, he would not rate his chances very high. And yet, so far—

He had fooled the Countess—or had he? In these dark hours of doubt, his uncertainty seemed endless. Yet he remembered her warmth, the intimacy of their last meeting. Surely if she had suspected— But he did not know how to complete that thought.

The church clocks tolled again. Three o'clock. Lying here dreaming of an alluring woman was hardly fit preparation for tomorrow's ordeal!

A car motor started up below his window. A car at this hour —was the gray sedan still there? Was he under suspicion? Was he going to fall into a baited trap tomorrow?

Five o'clock. He had missed four. Had he slept? He opened his eyes to see gray dawn poking tentative figures through the curtains, making the patterns of the deep Oriental rug faintly visible. He rolled over restlessly, regretting, as he did almost every morning, that a certain German general had a habit of sleeping late. It was torture to him to lie sleepless in bed. Quite suddenly a page of his voluminous notes flashed into his mind.

"On rare occasions, the General arises at dawn, possibly after a restless night, to take a long walk. Now and then, when he would prefer a drive, he orders the car."

Abraham B. threw off the eiderdown and sprang out of bed. Perhaps Paris could charm him.

He rang for his orderly and strode into the adjacent sitting room. Leaning over the desk to pick up a cigarette, he saw a note on the pad. It was from his orderly, timed twelve o'clock. Abraham B. had retired early; apparently his aides had not. Cryptically it read: "Close friend remains here—still searching for relatives." All of which meant that the gray sedan was still parked before the hotel; there was no line on its former occupants as yet.

The orderly slipped quietly into the room, looking as brisk and efficient as though he never needed sleep. He was fortunately very close when Abraham B. began in English, "Sorry, old man—"

The olderly threw up his hands in warning. Abraham B. shook his head in exasperation.

"You will order the car," he said, in precise German, meanwhile pantomiming his chagrin at the error and indicating his all but sleepless night. They could only hope that no listener, human or mechanical, was on duty at this hour.

Pulling away from the curb as quietly as possible, they watched apprehensively to see if they would be followed. After several blocks, they were still alone in the mist—almost alone in the world. Abraham B. began to relax and yield himself to the magic of Paris.

In the mist and at that hour, an illusion of peace lay over the city. The tight-faced, pale, hurrying throngs of the day were still finding what comfort they could in their beds. There was no one around even to cast a despising look at a limousine with German ensigns on the fenders, or at its three German-uniformed occupants.

Notre Dame loomed out of the mist. The exquisite ornamental sculpture upon those formidable towers was not discernible, yet it cast its majestic spell over them.

They could hear the low, chugging rhythm of a heavy diesel engine. It was a large, low barge plying the shallows of the Seine below Notre Dame. Farther along they came to a great circle and, in the center, the imposing Arc de Triomphe. As they drew closer to it, Abraham B. asked the chauffeur to stop. Perhaps the busiest part of the city during almost any day, at dawn the area was silent. Abraham B. got out and stood by the car, relishing the quiet. His senses were caught up by the freshness of the morning air. An aimless breeze was pushing back the mist. Following the breeze, his eyes looked in a direct line to the Place de la Concorde; in the gray dawn he could see the magnificent column of the Obélisque de Luxor.

He stood there a little while. Far off he heard the clop of horse's hoofs. He imagined the famous soldiers and rulers who had ridden into the huge Place de l'Étoile. The clop of horse's hoofs grew louder and a lone horse-drawn wagon approached. In time that sound died away. He did not know how long he stood below the Arc de Triomphe. He was brought alert by a yellow light within the Mercedes. The chauffeur had lit a cigarette.

Abraham B. returned to the car and stepped in. This quiet Paris—a Paris of whose existence many of its own people were not aware—had refreshed him.

15

Ten o'clock. It was time to start the serious business of the day.

After his early morning sortie into the mist-shrouded streets of Paris, he had found himself pacing through the General's ample quarters like a caged tiger. If the day held threats—his interview with Stuelpnagel, the mysterious occupants of the gray sedan, or even some result of his regrettable slip into English—he wanted to face those threats and have done with them.

He rang for the orderly. While he waited, he turned to study his reflection in the full-length mirror. His inspection was critical. Finally he nodded at his mirrored self.

Speaking now for the S.D. listening unit, he said crisply, "Call the military governor and request that he meet with me as soon as possible. Kindly advise General von Stuelpnagel that I am dealing with the most urgent business of the Fuehrer and require a personal meeting with him. Be certain that you inform his Excellency that this is a matter of High Command."

The orderly saluted Abraham B. as he walked away.

Infantry General Karl Heinrich von Stuelpnagel was military governor of France. He was subordinate to Field Marshal von Rundstedt for military matters only; in most other respects he was under the High Command of the Wehrmacht. Neither general had any authority over police or intelligence units; Heinrich Himmler directed such matters through his Security Service. The military governors had no contact with the Himmler departments, which kept the military governors out of the security sphere entirely. Higher S.S. and security officers kept up a careful observation of the Wehrmacht, which was little trusted by Hitler and Himmler.

During April, 1944, the German chain of command had been set up by Hitler and Himmler in a manner that kept all the responsibilities for the conduct of the war divided. Hitler apparently felt he could use one commander against another, and so prevent coalitions against him.

Field Marshal von Rundstedt was Commander in Chief West. Within his command were two Army groups: Army Group B, commanded by Field Marshal Rommel, and also Army Group H, commanded by Colonel General Johannes Blaskowitz. In the tangled line of command, the Third Air Fleet, under Field Marshal Sperrle, received its orders directly from Hermann Goering's headquarters. The Western Naval Command, under Admiral Krancke, operated by directive from the headquarters of the German naval staff. This arrangement meant that Rundstedt, though commander in chief, had no authority over sea and air.

All intelligence material was processed separately through General Zeitzler, chief of intelligence for the High Command of the Wehrmacht, headed by Field Marshal Keitel. No army group, like Rommel's, was permitted to work directly with the intelligence service, which reported directly to the High Command. None of these army groups had intelligence officers assigned to their staffs. This created an even wider gap in their intelligence liaison.

Abraham B. knew in advance that if he requested an immediate meeting with Rundstedt, it would be arranged as soon as possible; all matters of intelligence emanating from the Western Command must, by a standing order of Field Marshal Keitel, be cleared by Rundstedt.

Abraham B. crossed the room as his orderly worked the Parisian telephone; he slapped his suède gloves at his right knee, a mannerism of the General's when he felt in a forceful mood. Examining his image in the mirror, he said with a cynical smile, "The business of the Fuehrer must not wait for these incompetent idiots!"

He walked over to the bay window and looked out on the street below. The gray sedan remained. Abraham B. was alive to the impending action of this day. Yet as he stood there drumming impatient fingers on the curved frame of the bay window before him, his thoughts would not be confined. He wondered, where is she now?

Hooking the telephone with a resounding click, the orderly turned and walked over to him.

"Well?"

"His Excellency will see the General as soon as he arrives."

"The chauffeur?" asked Abraham B.

"In the waiting room downstairs, sir."

"Is the car ready?"

"Yes, your Excellency."

With that, they moved toward the door.

Abraham B. carried a dispatch case, the contents of which were as yet known only to him, his mission chief somewhere in England, and a small, highly specialized section of Allied intelligence working on a secret project that was in turn one part of the over-all plan called "Overlord."

"There are two men in the gray sedan," the chauffeur said, as he met Abraham B. Out in the open they dared to speak briefly in their own characters.

"We'd better keep moving—I'm not anxious to explain this," said Abraham B., handing the dispatch case to the orderly with what he hoped was a routinely casual action.

The three entered the limousine with the usual ceremony, the chauffeur managing several passing glances at the gray sedan. A moment later, they were moving ahead. Almost at once, the gray sedan pulled out and, making a U turn, followed.

"They're on our tail again." The chauffeur had seen the maneuver through his mirror.

"Nothing we can do about it now," said Abraham B., "but let's keep track of our shadow."

The offices to which they drove were on a short street, each entrance barricaded and manned by German soldiers. The building at which they stopped looked like an old-fashioned hotel.

The clerk who carried Abraham B.'s card to General von Stuelpnagel returned promptly to say General von Stuelpnagel would see his Excellency at once. Security guards escorted Abraham B. through two check points along marble-paved halls to the private, outer office. The sound pattern of their heels on the stone seemed like a metronome of fear to Abraham B.; he faced a crucial test. General von Stuelpnagel knew the real General by sight.

Abraham B. found himself in a large room, mahogany paneled and thickly carpeted. All sound seemed muted.

He faced several upholstered chairs and, opposite him, an imposing desk.

He heard voices in the next room. Without any signal, General von Stuelpnagel stood like a life-size picture as a large paneled door slowly, noiselessly slid open. He stepped into the room.

"Heil Hitler!" He paused. Would Stuelpnagel suspect anything? Did he now?

Stuelpnagel said, "Ah, pleasant to see you again so soon!" He moved to his desk and said in an assured voice, "Now, my good friend, how can I be of service?"

He sat at his desk, put on his reading glasses and, before Abraham B. could answer him, said, "Let me show you this memorandum from Wehrmacht Headquarters, signed by Keitel for the Fuehrer. I believe you have been out of touch."

Stuelpnagel had startled him for a moment. Abraham B. observed the direct look that Stuelpnagel held on him over his reading glasses. Stuelpnagel had long known that he was cut off from the S.S., the S.D., and German military intelligence. The information he held before him normally should not have been known to General von Stuelpnagel or his staff.

With a muttered sigh Stuelpnagel leaned forward. "Much of this is a mystery to me," he said. "Hardly any of these instructions pertain to my activity."

And with that, he handed the Keitel-Hitler memorandum across his desk to Abraham B.

"Do you have any idea what the object of such a memorandum is?" asked Stuelpnagel.

Abraham B. read the document. It dealt with elaborate train schedules for large infantry movements within France; it also included Panzer divisional movements.

Abraham B. said, as he handed the document back, "None; it must be principally for tactical commands."

Stuelpnagel removed his glasses and leaned back, no doubt hoping to learn something new, if only gossip, from the Fuehrer's headquarters. Abraham B. remained noncommittal and businesslike. He informed Stuelpnagel that he must have a meeting with Field Marshal von Rundstedt, and that it had to take place within twenty-four hours. Abraham B. was counting heavily on the belief that no one, not even a military governor like Stuelpnagel, would question the motives or actions of one of the Fuehrer's couriers.

"I shall arrange it without delay, General," said Stuelpnagel.

Abraham B. answered him, trying not to show his relief at that response. "Thank you. At this meeting with the Field Marshal, I wish neither army-group commander to be present. This is highly restricted intelligence. It must be treated according to the priorities set by the Fuehrer. Rommel will probably be informed later. Please inform the Field Marshal that this is urgent. I shall wait for your call."

"Of course, General. There will be no delay."

Abraham B. strode briskly back to the Mercedes. Could his

companions detect from his manner that he felt the mission was thus far successful? The chauffeur had kept the motor running. Now, as he drove off, they sat in silence. They left behind the dark silhouette of Notre Dame, but not the gray sedan that followed doggedly in the rear.

16

On entering the General's suite, Abraham B. devoted some time to a search for listening devices. It was nerve-racking constantly to wonder which innocent object might be sheltering a remote eavesdropper. He was now convinced that someone in the S.S. or the S.D. wanted a time and motion check on him; the familiar gray sedan was unsubtle evidence to that effect.

Abraham B. was aware of the distrust Hitler felt toward all the old Prussian clique. To advance within the hierarchy of a field marshal's headquarters, in any military capacity, still required a certain amount of the superior Prussian air, in spite of the fact that the Fuehrer had destroyed much of the Prussian veneer. Hitler had to restrict the Prussian fraternity to avoid its constant threat. One of his devices to keep control in his own hands was to provide his special envoys with certain extraordinary authority. Yet, it appeared, even the Fuehrer's official messenger could, in his turn, be under suspicion.

Abraham B. remembered the horrible accounts he had heard about the treatment of distrusted Germans. He devoutly hoped that Allied intelligence had made no mistake in believing that one of the few Prussian officers for whom Hitler still had respect, though he too was watched, was Field Marshal von Rundstedt. Yet even he, as Commander in Chief West, knew little about the strength or intentions of the enemy. The Western Command, having had no intelligence system of its own, found that its only source of such information was, by design, the High Command in Berlin. Allied intelligence was aware of this situation and indeed was prepared to gamble upon its inherent weaknesses, cramped within those narrow illogical bounds.

The orderly remained in the sitting room, at all times within sight of the attaché case. Abraham B. paced through the suite. He wondered if he had succeeded in covering up his surprise at the highly secret memorandum that Stuelpnagel had handed him. That document actually described a German deception plan, created for the purpose of confusing the Allied intelligence network on the Continent. Under this plan, French rail centers received actual instructions to transport mythical bodies of German troops. Various army-group headquarters in the West received actual orders to accommodate these same phantom troops. Army divisional commanders issued orders to disperse these phantom troops into the western zone, designating head-quarters for them. Large facilities were requested from the French housing agencies. Troop trains had been shuttled back and forth on schedule. If Allied intelligence was effective it would have evidence of massive troop movements. It would not know these were no more than paper troops, mere words.

Abraham B. had already worked out a plan to send word of this deception to Allied intelligence. Hardly had the plan formed in his mind when he discarded it. He could do nothing that might jeopardize his mission. He could only hope that his own deception had not been discovered. Had he made a mis-take? The opportunities for blunders seemed endless—Copen-hagen, Stockholm, Madrid, Biarritz, and now Paris. Desk clerks, sentries, innocent-looking civilians. Stuelpnagel, the gray sedan, the Countess.

And where, he wondered, where was she?

The ring of the telephone interrupted his thoughts. He heard the sturdy voice of the orderly speaking in an undertone in one of the other rooms. In a moment the orderly informed him that General von Stuelpnagel's aide had called to announce a hand-carried message was on its way from the Wehrmacht office.

Forty minutes later the orderly brought in the sealed envelope, which Abraham B. opened immediately and read. The body of the note called for an early morning meeting at the operational headquarters of Army Group B; its origin, Commander in Chief West—Field Marshal Gerd von Rundstedt.

Abraham B. walked to the dressing room. He removed a black leather case, thin and flat, which had been strapped under his tunic just above his belt line. From the leather case, he produced a key. He picked out a pair of the General's white kid gloves and, drawing them on, returned to the sitting room. He handed his key to the orderly.

The orderly had opened his collar and pulled out a ribbon on which hung a key. Applying both keys to the two locks on the attaché case, he opened it.

The attaché case had been delivered to Abraham B. in Madrid, but he had seen it before. That occasion had been near the end of his training period in England. It was then that he learned the reason for the special attachment that occupied almost one quarter of the interior space of the case. It was possible to open the case with the single key that he possessed; to do so, however, would ignite a compact but powerful incendiary bomb that would burn the adjacent document and, quite probably, anything or anyone else in the immediate vicinity. The second key, held by the orderly, disengaged the bomb and permitted the safe opening of the case. The special design of the case guarded against tampering. It could, should the need arise, be improperly opened to create a fiery diversion.

Before them now lay the document for tomorrow's ritual. There must be no flaw, visible or invisible. Certain fingerprints were already on it; they were not to be disturbed. No new prints were to be added. It was only necessary to turn over the pages carefully with gloved fingers, to make certain the document had not been tampered with during their guardianship.

All was in order.

17

The pale light of dawn on the following morning found the three Allied agents speeding through Paris toward Château La Roche–Guyon, some forty-five miles northwest. The silver moon, still riding high, peered at them as they drove along the cobbled roads.

The shadow of the Château La Roche–Guyon, or rather what it then stood for, fell upon the three long before they drew within sight of it. As they approached the Château, the morning skies were already blue with daylight.

Abraham B. was the first to notice the several black specks moving laterally across the southwestern sky. Now they saw columns of black smoke, licked by red tongues, rising in the morning light. Then they heard the whine of fighter planes!

The chauffeur slowed the car, swerved it over the road's shoulder and plowed about fifty yards across bumpy, hard ground toward a clump of trees. As the Mercedes came to a stop, the three leaped out and made for the cover of the trees' branches and new foliage. They had, for the briefest moment, forgotten their task and the Château La Roche–Guyon which awaited them.

When they reached the other side of the small wood, they saw the fast black planes banking to the south at treetop level about half a mile away, then darting down into the southwest.

The three men stood quietly watching. They waited about thirty minutes before resuming their journey.

The chauffeur swung the Mercedes into the private road to

the estate of La Roche–Guyon. The three in the car could see spread about them what remained of the once-beautiful gardens. Off in the distance lay the fields and orchards of the Seine Valley. Farther off, houses shone in the morning sun like cubes of white against the azure-blue sky. Security guards were posted systematically over the grounds of the château. The Mercedes approached the first barrier, a large guardhouse. Two surprisingly tall German soldiers, each with an automatic weapon, waited in front of them. An infantry colonel appeared, requested their credentials, then disappeared. It seemed that being the Fuehrer's messenger had little or no effect within the Château La Roche–Guyon.

They waited about ten minutes. The feeling of uneasiness bordered on fear which they hoped was not visible. What took so long? They were expected by the Field Marshal. The Colonel appeared again, entered another section of the guardhouse, picked up a telephone, and as he talked stared in the direction of the three Allied agents. The Colonel stood as erect as a statue. After some moments, he strode rapidly to the chauffeur's side of the Mercedes.

The Colonel seemed to realize, apparently through his last telephone conversation, that he had delayed one of the Fuehrer's special officers. Now he moved swiftly in an effort to wipe out the effects of the long delay. The security guard stepped back. The Mercedes eased along into a large, circular courtyard, was signaled to a parking area, and, before the car had completely stopped, was approached by an officer. He saluted and said, "Your Excellency, the Field Marshal will see you. This way, please."

Abraham B. followed the orderly carrying the attaché case as they were led through the large entrance hall of the château. The walls were hung with tapestries. Abraham B. was amused that, at this hazardous moment, he should recall that the château, a Norman stronghold built before the year 1000, was the family seat of the Duc de La Rochefoucauld. Undoubtedly on some wall was displayed a portrait of the most famous of the dukes, the author of the celebrated maxims.

In making this his headquarters, Rommel had picked a spot he fully realized the Allies would be reluctant to bomb; to doubly insure this, he permitted the ducal family to continue to live in the château.

Abraham B. and his orderly were led by their escort, the staff captain, to an anteroom, where they were requested to wait. Almost at once two other German staff officers appeared. They respectfully requested the General to follow them. Abraham B. sensed that they were being watched intently. Their guides continued to pace evenly down the hall. There seemed to be no suspicion that the impressive-looking General and his orderly might be impostors. Finally, they stopped before a large oak door. One of the German officers pressed a buzzer to the right of the door.

This was the conference room Marshal von Rundstedt had chosen. The evidence of Rommel lay about—a miniature model of an Africa Corps tank and a worn white scarf curled about a marshal's baton. On the large desk off to one side was a double portrait of a plain, pleasant-faced woman and a young boy— Rommel's family.

The orderly now carefully laid the attaché case on the conference table. The two escorts withdrew, leaving Abraham B. and the orderly under the surveillance of two armed soldiers.

Voices, then footfalls, could be heard drawing closer. Another critical moment had arrived for Abraham B. He moved toward the large French doors that led out to a rose garden. Beyond the window he noted two security guards.

Marshal von Rundstedt was surrounded by several officers as he entered the room. He greeted Abraham B. with a lazy, casual, almost unrecognizable, "Heil Hitler." Rommel was not among the group. Although he had never seen one of these men in person, Abraham B. recognized each. His mind raced over his picture-recognition file; no, the real Major General was not familiar with any of them. Abraham B. felt their intense stares while the Marshal's aide introduced everyone. After this brief formality, the staff group left, and Abraham B. now faced the imposing Field Marshal von Rundstedt—Commander in Chief West.

Rundstedt hoped his Excellency had had a safe and not too uncomfortable journey. Abraham B. detected an edge on that remark. How fortunate they could meet at the château; Rundstedt explained he had been on an inspection tour with Marshal Rommel, who, he was careful to point out, was not at the château but in the field, up toward the Channel coast defenses.

In appearance, Rundstedt was a man of more than average height. His head was large and well formed; his nose was of the classic Prussian boldness, which gave him a distinguished look. His thinning hair was gray and cut close to his head. His aloof air gave the impression that he was impervious to ordinary matters, men or problems. He moved with a certain mechanical precision. A puritanical Prussian. Abraham B. knew that he lived a frugal, quiet life. He was as strict with himself as he was with his men and officers; they respected him, were devoted to him.

Rundstedt motioned the two soldiers to leave. Without preamble he asked Abraham B. to state his business. Abraham B. realized that it was his supposed closeness to Hitler that made Rundstedt cool toward him.

Abraham B. asked his orderly to unlock the attaché case lying on the conference table. Withdrawing the key that hung around his neck, the orderly stood waiting. Abraham B. then reached beneath his tunic, withdrew his small wallet, and took out the other key. They approached the case and inserted both keys. With the case unlocked, the orderly saluted and left the room.

Rundstedt walked over to a large captain's chair, obviously not a part of the original château's furniture. There were several more like it about the conference table. He motioned Abraham B. into one, and sat down.

Before moving to the chair, Abraham B. reached into the open case, then turned and handed the Marshal a two-inch-thick, light gray script. On the front page were stamped the words OVERLORD—PART 1.

18

Rundstedt, as he scrutinized the document, paid little attention to Abraham B. What at first seemed diffidence quickly evaporated. He stood up, put a weight on either page, and continued to read, leaning on the conference table with his arms rigidly outstretched. At intervals, he went to the wall lined with bookshelves, removed a volume, turned to a specific page, read it, replaced the book, then returned to the document on the conference table.

The Marshal's intent reading ended abruptly. He faced Abraham B., his arms folded, with a steady stare and, with a nod toward the document that lay open upon the table, said pointedly, "Now, General, what is the source of this material?"

"This is, I am convinced, a bona fide Allied document. It was obtained in England through our agents."

"It must be checked in Berlin immediately for authenticity," said the Marshal.

Rundstedt looked steadily at Abraham B., who did not reply. The Marshal continued, "The invasion we face will prove decisive. I have repeatedly warned the Fuehrer of our imbalance, so has Marshal Rommel, but to no avail. Our forces are spread across too many defensive fronts; our reserves are limited. Those reserves must be held in the most advantageous positions for effective deployment. Anything less may mean doom."

Rundstedt briefly summarized his accounting of gloom at that moment in April of 1944. The Allies were advancing steadily in Italy, North Africa had long since fallen, Turkey was showing a disposition to go along with the Allies, and the entire Mediterranean must be considered lost. And the German forces on the eastern front had been forced back as far west as Romania.

Rundstedt led Abraham B. to the map on the conference table and pointed out that the front line of German defense involved nearly two-thirds of Europe. His shrug stated more eloquently than words that it was impossible to hold on every front. He walked over to the desk, selected a single page from a stack of papers and handed it to Abraham B. Across the top of the page he read:

THIRD AIR FLEET—WEST
  (98) ninety-eight bombers, operational
  (79) seventy-nine fighters, operational
  (420) four hundred twenty fighters, non-operational.

"Desperate," commented Abraham B. with feigned concern.

"It has been desperate for months," grunted Rundstedt. He reminded Abraham B., with ill-concealed pique, of his visit with the Fuehrer at Berchtesgaden during October 1943. That meeting was intended to stress the gravity of the military situation in the West. Hitler, however, who compulsively dominated all meetings, had soon monopolized the conversation, cutting off Rundstedt. The Fuehrer described the plans for the eastern counteroffensive. He discussed with fanatical fervor how the finest Wehrmacht divisions, with some 2300 of the newest Panzer units, would take part. When he finished, ecstatic and exhausted, he hurriedly bade Rundstedt good-bye and left. The Marshal had never had a chance to discuss the problems in the West. This had prompted him to write a lengthy appraisal of the western defenses.

In the memorandum, Rundstedt pointed out that the invasion could conceivably hit through northern France in the Calais area, through Holland or even Belgium, with its ultimate force driving directly into the center of Germany to the Ruhr. He suggested that the main attack might logically take place between Calais and the mouth of the Somme, pushing then through Belgium and the Aachen and Cologne gap. He further reasoned that Allied intelligence, through the French underground, had determined the true status of the coastal defenses in the area of Calais, which was alarmingly below any reasonable tactical strength. There had been no reaction at all from Hitler to the Marshal's report.

Rundstedt seemed to be taking a certain grim pleasure in having wrung from Hitler's courier the admission that the situation was now desperate. He made no effort to conceal his disdain of Hitler's irresponsible military decisions.

"What are we to do now?" he asked ironically. "The High Command believes May 18 to be the date for the invasion." After a few moments he added, "It would be a pleasure to think the Allies had actually presented us with a blueprint of their invasion plans. At least—if we could at last agree on it—our forces could then be deployed in strength at precisely the right places."

Abraham B. regretted that Rommel was not present. In fulfilling his role as Hitler's chosen general, he had had to insist to Stuelpnagel that the army-group commanders not be present when he saw Rundstedt; this was in compliance with the High Command's orders to clear all intelligence material concerning the western front solely through Rundstedt. However, Allied intelligence had calculated the document would have profound effect upon Rundstedt, who would share this extraordinary information with his entire staff.

Where was all this leading? Abraham B., now attempting a probe, casually stated, "This document has to be submitted to a complete authenticity check. I have brought it to you to reduce delays. But it will require time for a careful appraisal in Berlin, then a review by the Fuehrer's staff, and only then will it go to the High Command for action." Suddenly shifting to an incisive tone he pressed on. "I suggest that you might prepare in advance the steps I feel confident will eventually be ordered."

It was taking a considerable chance to push the Marshal so far. Yet Abraham B. banked on Rundstedt's unswerving sense of duty and his eagerness to accept a course that would promise a victory snatched out of imminent defeat.

"You have more confidence in the document than I do," retorted the Marshal. "Experience has taught me to expect the most refined machinations on the part of our enemy. A captured document could too easily prove to be no more than a dangerous hoax. I will move slowly."

With this dismaying pronouncement, Rundstedt fixed a wilting stare upon the General. Abraham B. felt that he paled, but he steadfastly met glare with glare. Had he, unknowingly, caused some seed of suspicion to take root in the mind of this venerable warrior? Was this Allied gamble doomed to failure? Were the odds against success simply too great to surmount? Rundstedt's shoulders sagged ever so slightly. He dropped his gaze and turned to press a button on the conference table.

"In any event, it is appropriate that the existence of this document be revealed to my staff," he stated curtly.

Abraham B. struggled to conceal his relief. If Rundstedt was going to share this information with his staff, he was more than half persuaded of its authenticity.

Calling for a table to be set beside a large wall map at one end of the room, Marshal von Rundstedt placed the document on it. Addressing his staff, he declared that he was not fully convinced, as yet, that an invasion would actually be launched in the Calais-Abbeville sector. But, he was quick to add, if the document was proved authentic, the Allied plan would follow the same pattern he had predicted in his October 1943 memorandum to the High Command.

Rundstedt then carefully outlined on the wall map what the

purported Allied document indicated. He detailed the plan that called for a massive, sustained attack in the Calais–Cap Gris Nez sector, preceded by diversionary landings that were to take place on the Calvados coastal sector to the south approximately nine days earlier, weather permitting.

The Allied plan specified the diversionary landing points— Pointe de Lornel, Berck, Le Tréport, Berneval, and Fécamp. Depending on the weather, other probe landings would be made between the Somme and the Bay of Saint-Malo.

Abraham B. was filled with admiration for the Marshal's extraordinary and rapid grasp of this fairly complex, highly detailed campaign of invasion. His clear, simplified presentation was evidence of a sophisticated military intellect. He said nothing to suggest that he suspected an Allied stratagem to convince the Germans that the initial landings southwest of the Calais– Gris Nez area would be merely diversionary, so that the Germans would reserve major defensive forces for the expected main attack at Calais. Indeed, if this elaborate hoax could succeed in massing German strength at Calais, then the main thrust of British and American landing forces more than a hundred miles to the west could gain an Allied toehold on the Continent. Rundstedt was outlining to his now mesmerized staff what he believed to be the Allied invasion plan called by the code name Overlord; in that tension-filled room, only Abraham B. knew the Marshal was actually detailing a hoax, a fraud, a deception; this was not Overlord.

Rundstedt drew the briefing to a close by emphasizing the dates given in the captured document. June 10, 1944, was set as D Day for the first diversionary attacks to the south and west, if the weather permitted. Also dependent on the weather, the main attack at Calais was to follow within nine days.

Rundstedt closed the meeting and ordered that the document be photographed immediately. He wished to keep a copy for his own use while the original went on to Berlin.

Before leaving the conference room, two members of the

staff paused briefly to speak with Rundstedt. Abraham B. overheard his comment to them: "I hope this Allied document is authentic. If it is, we may at last be able to operate this front in a military fashion."

Abraham B. could easily imagine the impatience in waiting for word, the eagerness with which Rundstedt would welcome the news that the document was authentic. His impatience, his eagerness will be no greater than mine, thought Abraham B. It was a part of his instructions that Rundstedt be persuaded to have the Allied papers hand-carried to Berlin in as rapid, safe, and impressive a manner as possible, preferably by a troop of S.S. Escort Commandos. Casually, almost indifferently, Abraham B. made the suggestion, picturing the irony of the situation if the French underground, working with Allied agents, intercepted the captured Allied document en route to Berlin.

19

He was rewarded by seeing one of the Marshal's staff officers summoned and instructed to requisition a troop guard immediately to hand-carry an invaluable top-secret Allied paper to Berlin.

The Marshal suggested that Abraham B. might prefer to return to Paris in the early hours of the next morning to avoid enemy planes, which were now frequently sweeping the area. He accordingly invited Abraham B. to remain at the Château La Roche–Guyon and join him and Rommel for dinner.

When an orderly came to inform him that dinner would be served in half an hour, Abraham B. realized that he had spent the entire afternoon reading, and though he found his surroundings the zenith of French perfection, he nevertheless felt the squeeze of tension, which wrapped about him like a cord.

The orderly returned and led Abraham B. to a large, formal dining room. Marshal von Rundstedt greeted Abraham B. as he came into the room and motioned him to the chair at his right.

"General, I believe you have met most of the men here. If there is someone you don't know, please tell me."

Abraham B. glanced slowly around, his mind taking quick inventory; the operations officer, Colonel von Tempelhof; intelligence officer, Colonel Staubwasser; the adjutant, Colonel Freyberg; technical staff members, Colonel General Lattman, Lieutenant General Dr. Meise, Lieutenant General Gehrke; and the naval adviser, Vice-Admiral Friedrich Ruge. And, of course, Field Marshal Rommel.

Abraham B. turned back toward Rundstedt.

"I don't believe I know the officer across from me, nor the officer at the end of the table."

Marshal von Rundstedt introduced him to the two officers.

Abraham B. looked over at Rommel, several places away, and thought to himself that this kind of dinner was unusual at La Roche–Guyon. Rommel was a man of simple tastes, ate wherever he found himself at mealtimes, and accepted whatever fare was offered. Unlike Rommel, Rundstedt's weakness was his sensitive and appreciative appetite. Rommel was asking Admiral Ruge how the German motor torpedo boat organization was progressing. Ruge looked about with an almost whimsical expression. "They're doing well, thank God; it's my whole Channel task force."

"Good. We must control the beaches," Rommel said, looking around the room. "The enemy will have the air and sea to their advantage. It's got to be strike, run, and strike again. Pressure, no pressure, pressure again."

Rundstedt added, "Maneuver and mobility will be the keys to our defense. Pas de Calais is fortunately adaptable for Panzer forces."

Abraham B. listened intently to these two extraordinary generals. Under other circumstances, he thought, he would have found a chance at such conversation a pleasantly thrilling experience. Tonight there was a sinister atmosphere.

Rommel turned to Rundstedt. "When the Calais sector is attacked, we can quickly bleed some of our occupation forces out of Belgium and Holland. . . ."

The next morning the Mercedes limousine made its way to Paris. For the second time the three Allied agents entered Paris in the early morning hours. They had, thought Abraham B., crossed their Rubicon. He smiled at his melodramatic imagery. He was no Caesar, and his two companions were hardly Roman legions. They were three men, three free men deep in enemy country. But there were legions, he thought, legions of men just like him, and soon they would be crossing a Rubicon and there would be no retreat. Hundreds of thousands of men. And the balance between their success and failure, their life or death, quite possibly depended upon his skill, his nerve, and his luck.

20

General von Stuelpnagel advised Abraham B. during the first afternoon of his return to Paris that special S.S. units, assigned from Berlin and Berchtesgaden, had reached Château La Roche–Guyon as escorts for the captured Allied documents. By evening the two special S.S. units had already left, one in the direction of Berchtesgaden with a photographed copy, the other toward Berlin with the original document.

Although the Allied team had never been able to locate the listening devices that must be there, they felt more comfortable within the General's suite than elsewhere. To maintain normal appearance, however, they must now and then venture out. Yet, as surely as their Mercedes swung out of the parking space in front of the hotel, so surely a small gray sedan swung out a few seconds later. They felt as if they were living in a surrealist world, surrounded by faceless eyes and with ears protruding from every object. Which was worse—the time of action or the time of waiting?

Yet the three men knew they must quietly endure this un-nerving period of waiting. A single miscalculation on their part in Paris, a single suspicion awakened in Berlin, and the value of the extraordinary document might be reduced to nothing. So, too, might their lives.

Two days later, there was still no news. Rundstedt had called Stuelpnagel to inform him of the pending evaluation, and to urge him to pass on any information that might come through his office. Both had been confident; now they began to wonder. Each time Stuelpnagel inquired, Himmler informed him that any information about the document would be released, like any other secret information, by the High Command in Berchtesgaden.

Even the three Allied agents began to feel certain qualms, although they knew of the carefully detailed estimate by Allied intelligence that it would take at least eight days for a thorough check of the document. And, added Abraham B., there is always the unpredictable.

That same day, unknown to Abraham B., a train rolled southward through France from Belgium under the gray cover of rain. Aboard was the Countess. The train was due to arrive in Paris the following evening. Was her journey routine—or urgent, perhaps desperate?

21

While Abraham B. waited in Paris, there were also those who waited in Berchtesgaden. The Fuehrer accepted the necessity of processing the document in Berlin and the need for the tedious delay before Himmler could satisfy himself of its authenticity.

As soon as a copy of the document reached Berchtesgaden, Hitler encouraged the key men of Keitel's military staff to study it and analyze its tactical and strategic implications. During this time Hitler appeared in better humor than anyone had noted in several months.

Hitler had optimistically accepted the Allied document the moment it had been revealed to him. And thus he fell headlong into the Allies' trap, exactly as they had anticipated.

Hitler, as he spoke to the gathered staff, stood before the tremendous fireplace. Lush coral carpets, covering the marble floors, enhanced the fiery setting. These dramatic effects seemed calculated to aid the strange, hypnotic power which he held over most of his staff. One by one each of them, including Keitel and Goering, voiced belief in his views.

Hitler played variations on the new and dominant theme, saying he had always foreseen an enemy landing on the Calais-Abbeville line, which justified his concentration of the stationary defenses in the Cap Gris Nez area.

The High Command sought to support the argument that the main invasion would hit just south of Calais. This was the shortest supply route for a smashing blow directly at the Ruhr and the German heartland. If Himmler had reported the captured Allied document a fraud, Hitler might even have tempestuously denied such a finding.

In Berlin, scientific personnel held vigil over the captured Allied document, now referred to as Project 669.

The geologists collected all detectable dust particles, comparing them with samples of soil from numerous locations. The chemists analyzed the ink—its dye, the water it contained, and its degree of hardness—to determine its composition and its source. The signatures were carefully checked through an extensive file system the Germans had meticulously built up over the years. The paper of 669 was analyzed, its fiber and weight revealing the time, area, and method of manufacture. The faintest fingerprints, exposed by X ray as huge blurred images, were doggedly studied.

Staggering amounts of data came from the study of these pages. Yet all the ingenuity devoted to analyzing the document had been more than matched by the forethought that had gone into its preparation. The document was indeed authentic; only its contents—and only a relatively small portion at that—were utterly false.

The first tentative presentation gradually swelled into a textbook report, dealing with geography, history, biology, economics, and strategy. This was no mere pamphlet, but a compilation of all available materials and reports relating to 669. It included tables of the American and British military lines of command. Anyone examining 669 would have been impressed with the strategic brilliance and tactical practicality of the military architects who were directing the Allied invasion of Europe. Project 669 was an entirely plausible, possible, practical plan for the invasion of Europe. It was, in fact, a carefully devised collection of calculated lies, coinciding in various degrees with the actual invasion plan Overlord.

Long before the check was completed and the report issued,

Himmler began to devote his cunning to the best utilization of the prize should it ultimately be proved authentic. The first step was to alert his agents and intensify their observations of unusual activity in London and Washington, D.C. He was keenly aware that the authenticity of Project 669 offered the perfect opportunity to perpetuate the myth of invincibility that Hitler and Goebbels had dreamed of for so long. If the impending victory was to appear the will of fate, not a whim of chance, an immediate step was necessary: to gag those who already knew something about 669. Himmler ordered Stuelpnagel to Berlin.

While Himmler was active, the Allied team in Paris and the German generals were left to brood, each in his own sphere. Nine days passed and no word came through from Berlin that the document had been processed through the severe tests of verification. After a fortnight of tense waiting, Abraham B. found that he was unable to contact Stuelpnagel. He had remained aloof from Abraham B. during their brief acquaintance; yet he had served the Allied team as the Paris link to the German war machine. His disappearance from the scene added another note of apprehension.

When Stuelpnagel reported in Berlin, he was instructed to remain in semiseclusion. He was not to return to Paris for several weeks; he was not to communicate with either Rundstedt or Rommel. This was necessary, Himmler explained, because of the need to verify 669 before any further action was taken. Himmler, in his preoccupation with the new promise of glorious victory, was unaware that Stuelpnagel concurrently was involved with General Helmuth Stieff, Lieutenant Colonel Klaus von Stauffenberg, and General Erich Fellgiebel in a conspiracy to assassinate Adolf Hitler. Several attempts on Hitler's life had failed. The executions of the known conspirators had been lengthy, viciously painful events. Yet, among certain of the generals, the belief that Hitler meant the doom of Germany persisted. Stuelpnagel and Rommel were among them. Thinking that possibly he had been found out, Stuelpnagel passed the information to Dr. Karl Stroelin, Oberbuergermeister of Stuttgart, who was then in Berlin preparing to visit Rommel at the Château La Roche–Guyon.

As soon as a given phase of investigation of 669 reached its conclusion, the specialists involved were shifted to other projects. Each of the specialists came away from the intense task with little more knowledge of the contents of 669 than if he had never seen a page of it.

Himmler had by now tested his idea on the Third Reich's propaganda minister, Joseph Goebbels. Himmler argued that a stunning victory at Cap Gris Nez could crack the enemy alliance; the Soviet might split away if the second front in the West did not materialize as promised.

Goebbels saw the potential in Himmler's plan. Hitler could be dramatized as the dominant military figure of modern times. Goebbels presented this prospect to Hitler at Berchtesgaden, describing the great role he would play as he directed the defense of the West wall against the Allies and crushed the June 10th invasion. Goebbels' idea further projected Hitler's military plan: The Fifteenth German Army and a large part of the Panzer troops would be held in reserve on the Calais-Abbeville line to impose a devastating defeat on the Western Allies. These two powerful forces would be strategically withheld from all preliminary Allied diversions; they would be committed only to destroy the main Allied invasion at Calais.

Goebbels' inventive mind had raced on; Rundstedt, Rommel, Stuelpnagel, and all the others connected with 669 would not be informed that it was an authentic Allied document. Hitler's courier general could be trusted to remain silent. The High Command would be under the personal direction of the supreme warlord, Hitler. The miracle weapons would be turned upon England, while the Allied invasion force was being dealt with by the German land army. Strategically, this would isolate Russia.

When the invasion was crushed, Goebbels reasoned, it would take at least a year for the Allies to mount another invasion of Europe. The United States might even be dissuaded from it. England, weary and drained, might easily sue for peace. Goebbels also pointed out that an abortive invasion would keep Turkey out of the war, neutral.

In addition to repulsing the enemy without, such a victory would consolidate Hitler's stature within Germany. No military figure alive could compete with his prospective glory!

Rundstedt and Rommel waited impatiently at La Roche–Guyon, Abraham B. waited apprehensively in Paris, and from Berlin and Berchtesgaden came only silence.

22

Underneath, Abraham B.'s thoughts still lived a life of their own and were at times given to daydreaming about the Countess. Outwardly, on this afternoon in late April, Abraham B. appeared only to be pacing rather grimly from one end of his Paris suite to the other. His orderly observed him and watched the matchless Oriental rugs for signs that a path had begun to show.

They were waiting—one walking to no purpose and the other observing nothing of particular interest. Waiting had become their way of life.

"If I telephone Stuelpnagel's office once more," Abraham B. exploded, "only to be told in that infuriating colonel's correct tones, 'General von Stuelpnagel has not returned from Berlin,' I'll send that infuriating colonel to Berlin to find him!"

He was releasing his pent-up emotion, but even this could only be done in character. They still had not found a listening device in the apartment, but they continued to speak for its benefit. Fortunately, the General could be at times explosive. And, fortunately, he would be as much annoyed by Stuelpnagel's mysteriously prolonged absence as was Abraham B.

Stuelpnagel was the courier general's military liaison when he was in Paris. He was in Paris a good deal. During the past two years he had spent as much as a month or two consecutively in Paris between the assignments that usually came from the Fuehrer through Goebbels, Bormann, or Keitel. On occasion, he was summoned to Berlin, although less and less to

Berchtesgaden; since February, 1944, only a handful of personnel were permitted to travel to Berchtesgaden because of the justifiable fear of assassination attempts.

As Abraham B. approached the end of another lap of his restless pacing, he stopped abruptly in front of the orderly. "Time to telephone."

"Might I suggest, sir, that you try a different tactic today? Suppose you should simply appear at Stuelpnagel's office unannounced."

"A capital idea! I will try it!"

Soon the Mercedes swung out of the parking space before the hotel, followed, after an interval of perhaps twenty seconds, by a gray sedan.

"The hounds are on our trail again," observed the chauffeur. It was now routine that the Allied team should be followed, yet they never grew altogether used to it.

Abraham B.'s unannounced visit to Stuelpnagel's office did not prove rewarding, although he sensed a certain amount of strain and worry in the faces of Stuelpnagel's staff. No explanation of his long absence was offered; one of the senior staff members suggested that General von Stuelpnagel might be detained by an old ailment which he had had checked in Berlin in the past. Abraham B. did not find this explanation very convincing and returned to the Mercedes more baffled than ever.

The three swung past the barricade at the end of the block and entered the main street, the swish of their tires on the wet pavement adding to the city sounds. The early evening air was soft, misty. In this half-light the crowds on the boulevard ignored the General's Mercedes, as well as the inconspicuous gray sedan that splashed along behind it.

Despite the rain, Abraham B. rolled down a window to drink in the smell of the city. Yet neither sight nor smell could divert him from the somber thoughts that oppressed them all. With Stuelpnagel's unexplained absence, they had lost their planned check point. They had thought the worst part of the mission lay behind them. Abraham B. had successfully put the false Allied invasion plan into the hands of the S.S. headquarters through Marshal von Rundstedt. Now, weeks later, the apparent success became doubtful and an oppressive sense of danger, impending disaster, pervaded their unvoiced thoughts.

They returned to the General's suite, where Abraham B. dressed for dinner. He was driven to the fashionable restaurant where he frequently dined. The General had often escorted the Countess there and it had been designated as the place Abraham B. should prefer while in Paris. He was fully aware, although the Germans were not, that the restaurant was one unit of the vast French underground.

Abraham B. welcomed the babel of voices, the rush of fragrant warmth, the familiar decor, as he entered the restaurant. Around the wall ran a continuous series of booths and tables. Everywhere he gazed he saw German uniforms. One more general caused no special stir, other than to evoke a slight deference from the haughty head-waiter, who led Abraham B. to a table.

Looking about the room now, Abraham B. could not have been more startled. In the soft light his eyes rested upon a woman in a group across the room. The Countess? Her back was turned to him; he could not be sure. As the moments passed, he found his senses mounting over the mere possibility.

Four White Russian musicians were entertaining, singing to the background throb of balalaikas. Abraham B. recognized the song as "Moscow Nights." Had the other listeners realized the title or the meaning of the Russian song, they would have registered strong distaste for the theme, but they seemed oblivious to it. Abraham B.'s gaze remained almost constantly upon the woman. He was certain she was the Countess. The quartet began a new song, playing and singing more loudly. The woman turned her head to one side as she talked to a companion. Abraham B. sat still, feeling the overpowering impact of her presence. His thoughts now raced. The actuality of this woman brought back piercing, warm memories to him.

As though summoned by a voice, the Countess turned toward him and caught his glance. In the soft light he could feel more than he could see the warmth with which she reached out to him.

Abraham B. rose, hoping he maintained the military stance of the German general, and walked over to the Countess' table.

"Please do not rise," he said to the several male guests, all of whom were in civilian clothes.

"General," said the Countess in a quiet voice, as she extended her hand. "It is so pleasant to see you in Paris."

Abraham B. smiled down at her. The host called to a waiter and ordered a chair for the General. The Countess then introduced the General to her companions. He waved aside the offer of the waiter to bring his service to the Countess' table; food now held little interest for him.

The host seemed shrewd and quick; the hostess was young and beautiful. Abraham B. forced himself to pay attention to everyone seated at the table. Having done so, he then turned to the Countess, smiling warmly as he looked into her eyes. "I have missed you very much. Why haven't I heard from you?"

"C'est la guerre," she answered.

Abraham B. thought this curt remark rather strange when he remembered the warmth in her eyes as she recognized him across the room. Why this sudden change? Some undercurrent in her relation with someone in the group? Or did it lie within her? Had she learned something in the past weeks to arouse her suspicion of him? If so, was she fighting, as he was, an inner conflict?

His uneasiness deepened. But there was nothing to do for the present except play out his role. Abraham B. conversed affably, if disinterestedly, with those about him. Only when one gentleman embarked on what promised to be a long rambling tale, did he yield attention to his tumultuous emotions. He tried to ignore them, but it did no good.

At last the hostess indicated the end of the evening. The group rose from the table and Abraham B. took the Countess' arm.

"Are you here with someone in particular?"

"No, I am not." Then she quietly added, "Yes, you may take me home."

They moved along, up the carpeted stairs, and onto the street. The rain had stopped. The Countess and the General said their good-byes to the group and stepped into his car.

Abraham B. reached for the Countess' hand. "Your hotel or mine?" he asked.

"Yours, if you like," she answered simply.

23

As they drove off, Abraham B. was fully aware that a new interlude with the Countess brought its own hazards. One was his almost reckless response to her. And there was the ugly possibility that she had already pierced his disguise. He dared not trust his own emotion. Yet, he wondered, how long could he deny it? Reason suggested the more prudent course of avoiding further involvement. He made a feeble attempt to follow it. Offering her a cigarette, he remarked casually, "Here you are, and now I may have to leave."

Despair shadowed her face. He recalled the same serious, concerned look when he had seen her last, that night they had spent together in Biarritz, a month earlier.

"Disappearing again when I most need you," she said with a wan attempt to smile. "If only I could have no feeling for you." She paused, then added quietly, "That's the pathetic part."

They both were silent, motionless save for the slight sway of the Mercedes. Not trusting himself to answer, he only gazed at her and caught the look of despair as she turned away.

The Mercedes slowed to a stop. They had arrived at his hotel. In the lobby the large white, red, and black Nazi flags hung quietly and menacingly in stark prominence. They passed through it in silence and gratefully entered his suite. He felt exhausted and for the first time in many days could have slept soundly. Standing quietly inside the locked door of the suite, he felt her confiding weight against his body. Her head lay cradled on his shoulder. At last he broke the long silence between them.

"I think I have searched for you all my life—and yet I do not know if I have found you. Will it be that we have only passed by each other's shadow?"

She lifted her head and looked long at him. "I can only say I found myself dependent upon you in Stockholm. I had known nothing, felt nothing for so long. Then you came—only to disappear again. Now I find you only to see you depart once more."

The Countess fell silent. He was filled by an undeniable feeling of desolation as he looked ahead. There was no escape. His predetermined path, if he were successful and very lucky, would be to leave France as stealthily as he had entered Denmark. Hers was a one-way drift back into Germany and, if he were successful, into its inevitable collapse. Their brief existence together would become a mere wistful memory. Liar, he said to himself, fool and liar!

At breakfast, over the thin French rolls and café au lait— which, thanks to the General's rank, tasted at least faintly of coffee—the Countess mentioned that she had intended to go to Crécy en Brie.

"To the same villa as last year?" Abraham B. recalled pictures of a charming old villa in the green river country; the folder holding them was labeled "General and Countess, Crécy en Brie." The villa, he knew, lay in the country east of Paris, actually between Lagny and Crécy en Brie. The Major General had visited the villa for days on end, and had gone there even when the Countess was in Sweden.

"The same," answered the Countess. "But truthfully, I had counted on finding you in Paris and persuading you to come with me. I shall give it up if you can't."

The French countryside in the spring! To share its magic with the Countess! This was a temptation Abraham B. had not bargained for. He knew he was rationalizing, yet he made no attempt to stop. Where else would the General go if the opportunity arose? And after all, it was dangerous anywhere he might be. . . . He would go with her.

On the pretext that he had a gay errand to perform—he actually went to a flower stall and bought a huge quantity of spring flowers for the Countess—Abraham B. managed a half hour of conversation with his two partners. Driving through the streets of Paris, they could feel momentarily shielded from listening devices or hidden eavesdroppers. Abraham B. revealed for the first time to the other two that their preplanned escape rendezvous point with a pickup team was tentatively set at Coulommiers, a small village to the east of Paris and just south of Crécy en Brie, not far from the Countess' villa. He told them that the date for the pickup, unless changed, was planned for early June. The Countess' invitation fell completely in line with the mission's schedule.

The three agreed that Abraham B. and the Countess should be driven to the villa and that the other two Allied agents should then return to Paris to await the call from General von Stuelpnagel. This would create the least suspicion within the Paris office of the S.D., which was presumably responsible for the almost constant watch placed upon the three men. They agreed that, as long as the Countess herself did not betray them, she actually provided them with the best possible cover against suspicion.

While Abraham B. completed his preparations for departure, he tormented himself with the question of how much the Countess knew or suspected of his impersonation. Was she, too, torn between duty and love? Was she, too, grasping this moment of perfection, in spite of the knowledge that it would soon be over and hopelessly lost? Whatever the future held for them was in the hands of chance. He realized the grim, thin possibility of it all.

* * *

The villa, its outer walls darkened and grayed by time, had a classic beauty in its simplicity. Two huge flower beds flanked the long, gradual steps up to the main entrance, a door of carved oak. The entrance hall was dominated by a circular staircase that led to the upper floors.

The Countess' suite reflected warmth and rich comfort. A four-poster bed, decorated by the "troubadour" motif, stood in the high-ceilinged bedroom opposite a white-tiled fireplace trimmed in robin's-egg blue. Running throughout the suite were thick Persian rugs of blues and reds. The polished floors were wide-planked, with wooden pegs. The red velvet walls were brightened by lights in crystal sconces. A mirrored dressing room led into a bath of white porcelain tile, patterned with an occasional gold fleur-de-lis.

Time, which in Paris had crawled for Abraham B., here at the villa had wings. Under a benign sun, the trees had feathered out almost overnight and soon shaded the bright banners of tulips along the garden paths.

Dressed in casual clothes, Abraham B. strolled here in the early morning before the Countess waked. Each bright morning he watched the townspeople who had set out to work in the surrounding countryside. Then he gathered a bunch of violets for the Countess' breakfast table.

Living in the villa with the Countess was a long, long way from reality. Or was this reality and his mission really a grim fantasy?

The first Sunday morning found Abraham B. pedaling down the villa's neglected and lonely road on his way to Mass. The General held to his family's tradition and, whenever possible, attended church on Sunday. This, Abraham B. reflected, put no strain upon his own nature.

As he turned onto the black-topped local road and felt the bracing morning breeze in his face, he was glad he had chosen to bicycle.

He passed several family groups wending their way in the

same direction. One man cautiously herded his wife and children out of the path of the bicycle; Abraham B. noticed his strong, pock-marked face and tall, slender frame.

Riding on, Abraham B. caught his first glimpse of the little church, his destination. Its spire reflected the rays of the sun knifing through the mist-wreathed landscape ahead.

Not far from the church, he passed an ancient cart drawn by a sway-backed horse. The driver sat in the cart; a second man, hat in hand, and an elderly woman whose head was completely cowled in a black cloak walked behind. Abraham B. saw a coffin in the cart.

During the service, Abraham B. noticed that the pock-marked man, sitting to one side of him two seats away, watched him intently until an older man attracted his attention and he looked away. Abraham B. suddenly recalled the cart. There was no coffin in sight within the church. There was no coffin to be seen when he left the church. He wondered about it, then thought how strangely his mind now worked, finding a sinister implication in events he once would hardly have noticed.

About a week after Abraham B. arrived at the villa, he learned that General von Stuelpnagel had returned to Paris and requested his orderly to make an immediate appointment for him. Although he was most concerned about the status of the false invasion document, which he had delivered a month earlier, he hoped to pick up other information that might help him and his team.

In a few days a meeting was arranged. The chauffeur and orderly called for Abraham B. and drove him back to Paris. Upon entering Stuelpnagel's office, Abraham B. sensed an uneasiness. He found Stuelpnagel tense and noted that his eyes were puffy and reddened, as if he had been sleeping badly. He did not, however, appear ill.

"You have not been summoned to Berlin?" asked Stuelpnagel.

"No, I have been relaxing in the country, giving the S.S. and S.D. surveillance teams that watch me a little fresh air." Abraham B. smiled.

"I doubt if they can spare many men to follow you these days," countered Stuelpnagel. "I heard unofficially that they have been busy in other areas of the Reich."

It was clear he was sounding out Abraham B., who did not guess how very alarmed he was over this unexplained report. Being himself involved in an assassination plot, Stuelpnagel was especially suspicious. He hoped the Fuehrer's courier might give him some clue as to what was going on. The one was as much in the dark as the other.

Neither of the two men who were now parrying each other's questions to conceal their lack of information was aware that by this time the false invasion document had become the tightly controlled and jealously guarded personal project of Goebbels. The document and its contents would remain secret. When Hitler ordered action to repel the Allied invasion, thus achieving a great German victory, only a very few people would know he had been guided by stolen plans. To the world, Hitler would appear the great and invincible military genius. So, at least, dreamed Joseph Goebbels. All Stuelpnagel could tell Abraham B. about the document was that, after some thirty days, it was still being checked by Himmler's staff. This was, in fact, as much as Stuelpnagel had been told.

Had the vast network of Allied intelligence miscalculated? If so, Abraham B. wondered why he had not been summoned to Berlin. Abraham B. had no way of knowing that Himmler and Goebbels had swiftly changed; from men at first seeking proof, they had now become the deceivers, withholding information from their own field marshals. Only in the event that there was some aspect of doubt would they have summoned the Major General who had originally obtained the stolen Allied document. There was no doubt.

But many doubts now assailed the three Allied agents. Was

their mission a failure? Were they in danger of imminent arrest? Should they alert Allied intelligence and, if so, how? Abraham B. and his two associates rode through the Paris streets, searching within their minds for some explanation, some guide for action. Over and over they reviewed events. Possibility one: The document was accepted as authentic but, for reasons not to be disclosed, it was being held secret. Possibility two: The document appeared authentic, but some lingering, gnawing doubt persisted in the mind of some intelligence evaluator and therefore the General was being closely watched to see if he would give himself away. Possibility three: The document was under grave suspicion and German intelligence was keeping the General in suspense so that no clue of the failure of the mission could leak back to the Allies. Possibility four . . . five . . . six . . . The series was endless; the more the team pondered, the greater their bewilderment.

At last they concluded they could do nothing but wait. Winston Churchill, during England's darkest days, had advised his countrymen to "hope for the best and prepare for the worst." A sound philosophy, but hard to apply when "the best" seems well-nigh lost and "the worst" cannot be predicted.

As the Allied team drove on to return Abraham B. to the villa, the three even wondered if they had become expendable.

24

Upon his return to the villa in midafternoon, Abraham B. and the Countess wandered into the neglected distant gardens of the villa. He was almost convinced beyond the last whisper of doubt that the mission was a failure, that their disguise had been pierced. If so, deception was useless. If so, nothing would be lost if he revealed the truth to the Countess and, in that truth, declared his love for her. But there remained a whisper of a doubt; perhaps the mission was still alive, still potent. Suppose, too, she already knew the truth and was playing a deadly game. He wondered to himself how he could destroy her, if it should become necessary.

They climbed a wooden stile at the end of what had been the rose garden, sat on its top step and gazed off across the fields. Peace lay over the land. They were on a little rise and could see, beyond the fields and over a distant wood, the spire of the village church. From their feet the ground sloped down to a little gully filled with runoff from spring rains. The only sounds were the sharp cries of four small boys chasing one another along the weedy banks.

She moved close to him and held his hand tightly for several minutes. This little time they had, he realized, might be their whole lifetime together.

When they returned to the villa, he lifted her hand and touched his face to it gently. Her eyes met his. After a moment, she moved easily into his arms. They held one another for a long time.

"It's all I could ask," she said quietly.

He looked at her and said nothing. Was she even now dreaming of their future together, surprised by the unexpected loveliness of this strange spring and all it seemed to promise? He knew the promise would fade by summer. Autumn, if he lived to see autumn, would be lonely and dreary for him. And for her? Her dark eyes grew moist. Did she suspect that the warmth he had brought into her life would soon be gone? She said, "I think I'm only beginning to know what love means, what love can mean. All these years, and now for the first time to know. So late, so very late."

And suddenly the floodgates of memory opened and the Countess revealed the strange and twisted story of her marriage. Her husband, she had learned to her early dismay, was a collector of time-killers, a wealthy, neurotic creature caught in a mad pursuit of pleasure and a flight from boredom. Their marriage had been no more than an incident in the young bridegroom's hectic journey. She soon found herself ignored, left alone, while he sought excitement in alcohol, women, and the thrill of high-speed cars. One fine spring day, accompanied by a woman who was never identified, drunk beyond control or caring, he raced his latest car off a canyon road and crashed through time's barrier into eternity.

The Countess had identified his torn body, but she could no longer identify herself. What was she? Who was she? In despair she too sought relief, drifting among strangers, turning to carnal pleasures because she did not believe in love. Men sought her and she gave herself, but the specter of the torn body remained. She could not commit herself to love; love was a mask and beneath it lay only torment and misery. And so she turned from man to man, from place to place, and at last returned to Germany, there to be swept into the mounting tide of the new Nazi state. She might have fled, but where was there to go? This was an insane world, but was hers not an insane life?

"Why do you tell me this? You don't have to."

"I want you to know," she said.

She then took both his hands in hers. "And now, so suddenly, so strangely to find you." What did she mean? She had known the General for years. He thought back, trying to reconstruct the moments, hours, days in which he had fallen in love.

"Listen to me," he said. "Of all the things I could tell you, or ever will tell you, this is what matters. I love you—for yourself—nothing else."

She looked away from him, holding back her tears.

He found himself back at the dreadful impasse, wanting to tell her who he really was. If he could not give her hope, at least he might give her understanding. He said nothing. He had no choice. He reached for her, held her.

The past years had brought no sweetness to her; as an adult, she had but the illusion of love she had cherished as a child. He longed to change this for her. Yet, as he held her, his mind was flooded by the terrible thought that a darkness was slowly closing in around them both. He would soon have to leave her without warning, without a word of farewell, with nothing.

Three days later, in the afternoon, he climbed the long, green slope that rose from the graveled terrace around the villa. The grounds were thick with growth, the grass in the distant fields wild and long. He trudged along, feeling the need to dispel his discouragement. He suspected that the Countess, sitting by a window gazing at the cloudy sky, was as miserable as he. After he had walked some time, he came upon a sudden rise in the path and realized he was some distance away from the villa.

As he turned his attention away from his own dark thoughts, he saw two men moving along in a direction diagonal to his. Their sudden appearance startled him, aroused a sense of danger. Why should two men be in that field with him, away from the road, or farms, or any obvious destination?

The two silent figures moved along at a slow, steady pace. Abraham B. kept on moving mechanically, trying to measure whether the men meant him harm or not. It was not uncommon for the French underground to do away with a German, and especially an important one. It would require little detection to learn that Abraham B. was a high-ranking general officer.

The two men were drawing closer, moving in upon him. He was now tense, every sense alive, realizing that he was very nearly trapped. To fight two men who might be armed was useless. To run or hide seemed attractive but practically impossible.

He shifted toward the road to his right, maintaining the same even pace. Once within sight of the road, he increased his pace, walking as fast as he could without running. The two men equaled his speed and moved toward the road. Abraham B. was now aware that their path would soon intersect his. He glanced about, trying not to reveal unusual concern. He noticed that he was out of sight of the villa, having gone down the other side of the long slope. There were two farmhouses in sight, but a man who spoke French with a German accent was an enemy here. He could expect no haven. He calculated that there were about twenty minutes of daylight left.

He was momentarily reminded of the field in Denmark when he had moved silently to his rendezvous point. He had felt the menace then; he did now. He was cold with fear. Two strange men. How many days had they waited to meet him there? When would they attack?

He looked back. They were still coming toward him. In the distance up the road he saw the poplars ranged to one side. About a mile ahead stood the woods, almost black, with only a tinge of dark green from the fading light of day. Beyond the woods was the church, its narrow spire now cut off from his vision.

Abraham B. guessed he had no more than ten minutes of daylight. His eyes swept the terrain; he decided he would take any ravine at full run, hoping he might lose them in the deepening dusk. He cast another look behind him and realized that the two men were gaining. They had reached the bottom of the slope as he moved onto the road. Once there, he noticed a small channel that crossed under the road and ran a meandering course in several directions. The grass grew higher along its sides.

Abraham B. jumped into the stream bed and began to run, but even as he ran, he managed to grab a heavy stick that lay in the channel. He had feared gunplay, but much to his surprise he heard no shots. One glance revealed that the two men were in pursuit along the same path he had chosen.

He hadn't run for many minutes, but his breath was now heavy, his mouth dry. Daylight had almost gone when Abraham B. saw a small footbridge which would take him across the channel. He leaped onto the wooden span and, to his horror, it yielded under the impact. Off balance, unable to break his fall, he found himself on the bottom of the muddy, two-foot-deep stream. The soft, semirotted wood had made almost no noise as it gave under him. He lay numb and still. He saw his two pursuers lunge by in the semidarkness, guided by their last clear look at the man they now could neither see nor hear.

As the minutes passed, he could still hear them ferreting in the dark, off in the countryside. Then the quiet of the night was rent with air-raid warnings from the far distance, and soon after he heard Allied planes heading south and east. The sound of the planes manned by his compatriots brought a small spark of comfort to the harried man in the ditch. He looked at his watch, decided he would wait for fifteen minutes and then, if all was quiet, move out cautiously.

Abraham B. quietly groped along the side of the small channel. He rose as silently as he could, with the muddy, cold water washing down from his clothing. It took him a few minutes to gain his bearings. With all the stealth he could manage, he made his way back toward the villa.

Why hadn't they shot at him? Why had they merely chased

him? French underground? Or Gestapo? Did they want him intact and alive? Was there any safety at the villa?

He proceeded with the utmost caution, but there was no sign of his two strange adversaries. Once inside the villa, he moved hurriedly up a dimly lit stairway. He didn't want the Countess or any of the servants to see him. Tomorrow he could excuse his muddy clothing casually, a mere slip into an irrigation channel along the hedgerow.

He bathed, dressed and went down to the library where he waited for the Countess. A deep sense of danger haunted him through the quiet, tender evening, beyond the caress of wine and the hearty embrace of brandy. Only the warmth of the Countess beside him and the oblivion of sleep gave him release.

25

A damaged shutter, adrift in a burst of early morning wind, banged and rocked against the rain gutter, breaking the softer country sounds of a new day. Opening her eyes, the Countess whispered, "One need not shout so early in the morning."

Abraham B.'s laugh was easy and gay and contagious. The Countess burst into joyous laughter. The two had reached a rare communion of spirit.

In the windy mid-May afternoon, the other members of the Allied team arrived, and Abraham B. reported what had occurred the afternoon before, describing in as much detail as possible the chase across the distant field. He told them of his fear during the weird encounter; his pursuers had been like two ghostly creatures fouling the lovely countryside that heretofore he had thought so peaceful, so empty of threat. Candidly he confessed to a sense of impending danger that even now he could not shake off. But what of Paris?

His two associates reported that Stuelpnagel was again absent from his office. This raised the potentially ominous question: Why? Did his absence relate to them and their mission? They could not avoid the fact that Stuelpnagel's unusual behavior had started shortly after Abraham B. had turned over the invasion document to Marshal von Rundstedt; they had no clue about what had been concluded at Berlin headquarters, although they were certain there must now be definite findings. They could only view this continuing lack of information with increasing alarm. They could have no knowledge that Stuelpnagel's current absence concerned rebellion, not invasion, though they would have drawn some comfort from knowledge of the secret meetings that promised a collapse of the Nazi machine from within.

Stuelpnagel in mid-May was meeting with Rommel and both their chiefs of staff in the outskirts of Paris, discussing ways to blot out National Socialism within Germany and reach an armistice in the West. This conference took place in a country house in a village called Mareil-Marly, near Saint-Germain. They reviewed the complex problems to be faced in such a revolt, and decided on certain policies—but only in theory.

Shortly after this meeting, a visitor from Berlin came to Château La Roche–Guyon. General Edward Wagner, Quartermaster General of the Army, had come to evolve the necessary plans by which Army Group B and the High Command of the Army would co-ordinate their parts in the impending revolt. General Wagner informed Rommel of the several abortive attempts on Hitler's life, all of these highly guarded secrets in Berlin and Berchtesgaden. He felt strongly opposed to an assassination of Hitler, fearing this could make a martyr of him; Rommel held that Hitler should be arrested and tried by the German nation.

Château La Roche–Guyon had many visitors; they came almost daily. They spoke of a ravaged and decimated Germany. Most of them had once been credulous and enthusiastic Nazis, although a few had been anti-Nazi from the beginning. One of these latter was General Alexander von Falkenhausen, an intimate friend of Rommel and Stuelpnagel's, once their teacher at the infantry school at Dresden, now military governor of Belgium and Northern France.

These initial preparations led to an even more important meeting, held in the Black Forest of Germany. Its difficult task was the selection of a leader for the revolt.

One evening in late May, a certain house in Freudenstadt was quiet and dark, to all appearances empty. Inside the entrance several officers of Marshal Rommel's staff maintained an intense watch. They would allow no intruder past the entrance hall of the quiet house.

On the second floor two other officers stood guard outside a closed door. Beyond the door was a spacious but simple sitting room. The glow of a fire provided the only light. Among the shadows, three men sat quietly discussing the future of Germany.

General Speidel, Field Marshal Rommel's chief of staff, had journeyed to Freudenstadt where he had joined Baron Konstantin von Neurath and Dr. Karl Stroelin, mayor of Stuttgart. Their discussion concerned the likely men to take the lead in the overthrow of Nazi Germany. Of all candidates, Rommel appeared the most popular and possibly the most acceptable to the Western Allies.

They also discussed the available avenues for approaching the Western Allies: Allen Dulles of the United States in Switzerland, Sir Samuel Hoare of Great Britain in Madrid, or the Vatican in Rome.

They considered the relative merits of Rommel's view that Hitler should be arrested and prosecuted by a German court of law and the contrary view that he must be done away with in haste to offset a possible long-drawn-out civil war.

These three Germans were also concerned with establishing channels of communication with the various secret groups known to be plotting against Hitler.

The fire burned late that night in Freudenstadt.

26

It was late afternoon the day after Abraham B.'s strange encounter with the two men. The three Allied agents walked into the nearby fields. Before them the grass was fanned by the wind. They had been silent for several minutes when the orderly spoke, sending a small covey of partridge into fitful flight. Looking toward Abraham B., he said, "The German radio is blacked out."

"What sort of transmission have you heard?"

"Just the endless code quotations from London, like 'State the nature of your business' or 'Who sends Harvey to me?' Another was, 'René is on the bridge on watch' and 'George stands at the rail and shouts.' It goes on continuously, repeated in French, English, and German."

Abraham B. regarded this with disinterest. It had been decided long months before that the Allied team would not use any type of radio for communication after their departure from Biarritz. From that time on any contact would be made through a special French underground unit. The Allied team had no knowledge of that unit; all the three agents knew was the recognition signal.

The Sunday following the incident of the chase, Abraham B. and his orderly set out on bicycles for the small village church; the chauffeur remained at the villa. Off in the distance they saw three children running over a stile, headed for church. The peaceful panorama was disturbed only by the silhouette, far off, of a German troop convoy of a dozen trucks. The early morning sky was sunny and cloudless. As they pumped along, the orderly a little behind Abraham B., they looked like stiff, animated puppets, heads bent forward, pistonlike legs moving rhythmically. Ahead of them, a half-mile away, stood a long line of poplars that ranged toward the horizon and seemed to vanish into it.

The morning air was suddenly cut by an intruding noise. Three fighter planes hove into sight, heading in their direction above the distant trees. The deafening roar of the plane engines rocked the air. The whole countryside seemed to shake with the sound.

Abraham B. jumped off his bicycle, letting it go bounding on until it fell on its side. Running, he jumped a ditch and headed for a distant farmhouse, motioning to the orderly to follow. In theory, they knew, Allied planes would not strike civilians; in fact, they knew that the view from a fast-moving plane is not very clear. Like all groundlings in this war, they looked for protection, realizing that theory means little to a corpse.

The orderly had jumped a split second after Abraham B. and was about twenty paces behind him, running in the same zig-zag line. As the planes swept down, they both dove to the earth, their arms outstretched like divers in a shallow lake. They dropped out of sight in the tall grass. Abraham B. looked up as the planes passed overhead. In a fleeting second he saw the round insignia of the R. A. F. on the underside of the Spitfire's wings. The planes were gone as fast as they had come, their thundering roar fading away.

From the distance Abraham B. could hear the faint sound of more planes approaching. Jumping to his feet and signaling the orderly, Abraham B. headed for the white farmhouse some fifty yards ahead. The two twisted and danced their way in a crouching run. The noise of planes now rose in a second crescendo. The racing men had just reached the house site when the new wave of Spitfires passed overhead. Both men were breathless as they lay upon the ground alongside the small structure. At last the strident sounds of the low-flying aircraft diminished, then faded away.

For a third time the sound of approaching planes scarred the air. Abraham B. and the orderly saw a man running toward them. As the stranger neared the house, the roar of planes again reached a peak. The man, wearing the garb of a chimney sweep, rolled on the earth about ten paces away from where Abraham B. and the orderly lay. He, too, had traded the country road for the feeling of security the little white stone house seemed to offer. Like a clap of thunder in a summer storm, the noise that had spread across the country passed over them again.

Abraham B. recognized the stranger as the pock-faced man he had seen on his first journey to church two Sundays before. As then, the man's expression was somber. He lay propped up against the white rock wall of the small house staring at the two Allied agents. He continued to stare at them as the noise of the planes again fell away. For the first few moments, anyone might have surmised that the three lay silent because of the breath they had squandered in their dash for safety. Then Abraham B. noticed the pock-marked man slowly turn his bony hands, palms down, to the cold ground. He seemed to be readying himself for a sudden, quick move. As he did so, he fixed a disconcertingly intense look upon the two.

The two Allied agents were equally tense. If they had to make a move, it would be to kill. They were grateful that killing had not been necessary thus far, but the possibility had always existed from that first moment in Denmark. This might be the first time. Why, Abraham B. thought, a Frenchman? Or was this a Frenchman?

After perhaps a minute, and without moving, the pock-marked man began to speak. "Do you see the thumbs upon my hands?"

Abraham B. saw a look of relief on his orderly's face. Then he said, "Are you sure there are only two thumbs?"

The man answered, "No, three thumbs!"

Abraham B. felt jubilant, but he continued the prescribed ritual. "Are you concealing anything?"

The man responded, "Yes, the darkness."

At that moment, Abraham B. and the orderly knew they had met their French underground contact.

"How shall we call you?" Abraham B. asked.

"François," he replied. "Do not move, I beg you. We may be watched."

Not one of the three men made a further move. There was no sign of life within the little stone farmhouse or nearby in the fields.

"June 10 will be the night," François said. "I shall tell you the time the day before, or any change that might occur." François paused, then continued, "You are under constant surveillance by the Gestapo in this area, but you need not fear the fields around the villa."

"Who tried to take me out there?"

"Those two men were French," said the man quietly but pointedly. "They were trying to contact you that day, but they were signaled from a distance that the Gestapo had all three of you under binoculars. So they began to chase you. I'm glad you ran for it. It would have been very difficult if we had caught you."

Just then the church bells were heard. The strokes were distant, yet clear and distinct. François stared hard at the tranquil morning sky, now empty of planes or clouds. Suddenly, with the agility of an acrobat, he jumped to a crouching position. Turning quickly to the other two, he said, "I'll go by the field now. Until later, au 'voir."

He was gone, the dust he ruffled up quickly settling. The other two rose. Abraham B. dusted off his clothing, and the two moved toward the road to retrieve their bicycles. They had missed church, but they felt immeasurably comforted by their encounter with François. Abraham B. looked about. Except for the two of them, not a human soul was in sight.

27

Grown impatient with the grumbling of the storm and the useless effort to sleep, Abraham B. had left his bed and, after throwing a heavy coat over his shoulders, had gone out onto the terrace. The rain was cold. The weather had blustered three days now—since the first of June. He thought of the thousands of miserable men across the Channel, waiting, waiting in the dreary rain, even now wooing a fitful sleep. By contrast, he thought, his hardships were light. In not too long a time, while he still waited, they would be locked—the time-worn phrase had never seemed more appropriate—locked in mortal combat. The fate of the world, no less, hung in the balance.

Shivering in the chill wind, he turned and went in, feeling the wind press strongly against the French doors as he closed them. He stood there, facing the doors and leaning on the long, curlicued door handle. In less than a week, if fate were kind, he would leave France. If fate were kind, he thought! If fate were kind he would never have met the Countess, or she would have been someone else, someone really like the woman described in the dossier at Allied headquarters.

He could go to her now; he longed for her, for the comfort she could give him. But he was tormented by thoughts that transcended his passion, his pain. What would become of her? After the bitter hurt of his sudden departure, his disappearance without warning, without explanation, what hurt would follow? What dangers lay ahead for her? What personal tragedy loomed in the national tragedy he was sure must come? If only he could stay, remain with her, even to a grim, all-too-quick ending. His own life, he thought, was not so much to lose, but thousands, hundreds of thousands of lives—no, the odds were clear; his course was fixed beyond his choosing.

He walked slowly into the library where the pale light from the fireplace flickered like a beacon. Two great logs they had put on during the evening still glowed companionably. He threw on a smaller log and stood there staring while the fire took hold.

Gradually the warmth reached him. He slipped off the wet coat and draped it over the bronze fireplace tools. He took a candle, lit the candelabra, and slowly walked about the room, seeing in the soft glow things he knew he would remember until the day he died. He had grown fond of his somber room, its dark polished oak, the rare old books with their leather bindings. Perhaps, if only in memory, he could take refuge in this room.

He paused again before the fire. How complete their life could have been together! The license that war grants for brutality and the dismissal of convention no longer had meaning. Her concubine existence, no matter how justified before, would now be a lie and mockery. She was no more the same woman he had encountered in Stockholm than he was the same man who had dropped from the skies of Denmark. He could neither deny nor turn away from his passion for her. Now it was too late to question how far their love might go.

An hour passed and still the storm raged. Finally he looked for a companionable book. Taking a volume of Victor Hugo's verse, he settled in front of the fire. He turned the pages, looking for a favorite old poem. He heard a sound, a rustle behind him. For an instant he was frozen. Then he heard the words of the verse in the Countess' voice coming from just behind his shoulder:

" 'J'étais seul près des flots, par une nuit d'étoiles.' A poem by Hugo. You have changed so very much—General." There was a slight pause before, and a more than slight teasing quality to, the word "General," which she had not called him for many days.

It could only mean what he dreaded to believe.

When he chose the Victor Hugo volume, he had thought there was no chance of his being found with it by anyone— least of all the Countess. The real General preferred German literature; he was particularly contemptuous of French poetry.

If fate were kind? No, fate was being vicious. Thousands, hundreds of thousands of lives about to be cast into a fantastic gamble. He held a secret that could destroy those lives, and now, in a real sense, she held it too. His instructions were explicit; they left no margin for choice, not even for argument. It was his clear, sworn duty to kill the Countess. Kill? No, he thought, the word is murder.

He felt physically ill. Cold sweat covered his forehead. His mind twisted into a spinning, sickening, whirlpool of conflicting thoughts and emotions.

Gallant men converging on England's beaches. German heavy guns leveled at the sea. The Panzer Corps poised for attack. Duty. Overlord. Duty. Love. Murder. Love. Dear God! Dear God!

The Countess laid her hand on his shoulder. She saw on his face signs of the pain that he could not speak of.

"Oh, my dearest, forgive me! What have I done to you?"

"How long have you known?"

"Since Biarritz, perhaps even Stockholm."

Once more his mind was spinning—backward, then forward.

"What do we do now?" he asked. For him, the moment seemed unreal; he wanted to push it away, run from it. She seemed to have taken heart from his use of the word "we." She hesitated, then said, "I have one wish."

He attempted to stop her, but her fingers touched softly on his lips, pressed gently against his mouth. "Hear me, I beg you."

He waited for her to speak. He could not trust his voice.

"Marry me."

"Why? Why now?" he asked from the depths of confusion.

"For a long time, too long a time, I have not cared what the world thought of me. But if I could belong to you, before God, I should be content to die."

It was only then that Abraham B. understood the enormity of his misjudgment of this woman. She could have betrayed him a hundred times before now. She had known almost from the start, yet she had protected him, saved him, and knowingly permitted him to complete his task. She had not confronted him with her knowledge, had not pried, had not even hinted. She had blindly accepted him, yet in that blindness she had known more truth than he, liar and fool, had perceived with all the facts before him. She had placed her trust in him, in love. He was now committed to betray her, betray love.

He looked at her, then enfolded her in his arms. They sat silently for a very long time, clinging to each other. Finally he said, "I still don't understand."

She turned her head up to him. He saw a resolute look touched with recklessness.

"I love my country," she answered. "But this barbarity, this madness is not my country. It is a deadly sickness that has come to Germany. I do not know what you are doing. I do not ask. But I have trust in you. What you would do will finally expunge this disease. Germany will return to humanity. It will be a painful, horrible journey, but only, I pray, for a little while. There is no other way."

Abraham B. felt his last doubts washing away before her candor. She was no spy, using her charms to seduce him. She was a woman, once strangely lost, now as strangely found. Whatever her past, when faced with the fatal choice she had simply, silently, and irrevocably placed her faith in love and the cause of freedom. He now faced as fatal a choice. Or was it

147

a choice? There would be no meaning to his life, his mission, this world-wide struggle if indeed this was a question of choice. He knew with complete conviction what he must do.

"I don't suppose we can get the priest in this storm?" he said.

"Your chauffeur could make it, in the morning, in my Opel. The road will be abominable, but there will be little danger of planes."

"I'll send my orderly. He will be going to Mass and can speak to the priest afterward."

In the stillness of the room they could both hear the rain, less violent now, drumming on the windowpanes.

"Must you—go soon?"

"That you must not ask," he said.

She turned from the room and the low fire. It must be almost dawn by now, Abraham B. thought. He could just make out her form in the darkness that surrounded the staircase. He had to be very certain of the exact course he would follow. Before he yielded to sleep he must know precisely what he would do. If ever he were to think clearly, let it be now, he prayed.

Abraham B. awoke after a fitful sleep to find the storm had diminished and morning light was creeping into the library. The fire was dead. He rose from the chair, grunted at his stiffness, then quietly went upstairs to his room. When he had dressed, he rang for his orderly and explained the need for a conference.

"An unforeseen turn," he began, frowning, when the other two had joined him. The orderly and chauffeur looked at each other apprehensively. "Our new problem is that the Countess is determined to marry me. Without delay."

The chauffeur whistled. There were perhaps three minutes of silence as the two agents considered this wholly unpredicted situation. Only then did the orderly, with something close to elation, burst forth.

"But that's perfect! A wedding celebration, no matter how quiet and simple, will provide an excuse for a few local visitors and any unusual movements on our part. It's an ideal cover-up and just when we need it. We haven't much time left—and when we move at last, we'll be a lot less likely to arouse suspicion or even to be taken seriously. Really perfect!"

"Hold on," said Abraham B. "This may seem perfect to you, but you're not the groom. This means a real wedding ceremony, a sacrament of the Church. It's nothing to be taken lightly."

"Neither are the lives of thousands of men," replied the orderly, "and they're the stakes in this gamble. I know this is the most irregular part of an already weird game, but I think fate is playing into our hands. Besides, think of the risk if you refuse and we are invited to leave here and now. Frankly, I don't think you can risk refusing."

Abraham B. walked to the window and stared out. He had to make it appear that he was weighing his decision with utmost care. He counted slowly to two hundred. Then he turned to his two confederates.

"I agree," was all he said as he walked from the room.

28

For the orderly, Abraham B.'s suggestion that he attend Mass that Sunday morning and ask the priest to come to the villa, offered a welcome relief to the tedium. All had agreed that it would be risky for him to take the Mercedes, with its General Staff insignia. In the Opel, the orderly moved along the country track at a cautious speed. He had to watch the mired road closely. Along the road's edge were soft, muddy shoulders. His progress as he splashed along was not unmarked. He was in fact being shadowed by two men who had every intention of knowing what took place in the villa.

Parked on a side road, a little less than a quarter of a mile away from the villa, their gray sedan was half hidden by the branches of a chestnut tree. When they identified the orderly through their binoculars, the driver started the engine, preparing to edge to the next vantage point.

Their movement in turn set off another. François, the pockmarked man, had given orders that the Gestapo agents were to be watched constantly.

It took the orderly a good quarter of an hour to reach the small village. He drove slowly through the square across the cobblestones, then brought the Opel to a stop. He walked several hundred feet to the church and entered through the wide double doors.

The church was silent except for the creaking of the doors as he closed them behind him. There were few of the usual Sunday morning worshipers to be seen. He turned to the left and walked down the side aisle to a small side door to the left of the altar, then entered a small, oval area. The atmosphere here was oppressive. The only light came from a high, narrow window. On three long, scuffed tables lay three crude wooden coffins. An elderly man sat motionless, almost hidden by them. A fourth coffin lay at his feet.

The orderly stopped short at the sight of the still figure. He stood there quietly weighing the implications of the strange scene. Outdoors, he could hear the rain and wind beating on the church walls.

A small door slowly opened on the other side of the room. The priest quietly entered, looked to the orderly, and nodded. The priest was a man in his middle fifties, slightly bowed, with a benign air. He was wearing a black robe with a white ruff; there had apparently been an earlier service that morning. While he removed his ruff he glanced about the room. Still the expression of the old man remained unchanged. The room was so quiet that the orderly felt eerily alone in spite of the two silent figures.

As suddenly as he had appeared, the priest turned back, without saying a word, and went into another room, beckoning the orderly to follow.

The priest moved so rapidly that the Allied agent had a strong impression he did not want to remain in that part of the church any longer than was necessary. The priest opened another door and entered a smaller room. The orderly followed. Once inside, he was motioned to sit down.

This was a private sitting room, no larger than a good-sized closet. It was simply, even crudely furnished. As he looked down at the floor momentarily, he noticed wet tracks on the paper-thin rug. The priest sat down on a swivel chair, cupping his knee in both hands.

"And so?" he asked.

The orderly spoke in French. "The General has asked me to request that you kindly return to the villa with me. I hope it is convenient for you, Father."

"I presume it is an urgent matter?"

"Yes, Father."

The priest pulled out his watch, studied it, and then turned back. "Very well," he said loudly, "we will go after the services."

"Thank you, Father." The orderly rose. Seeing that the priest did not, he waited.

The priest looked up at him and said, "You must wait here for me. I hope you will not mind."

"As you wish, Father." Why, he wondered, was he not being allowed to attend Mass?

The priest excused himself, rose, and went out into the church, leaving the orderly to wait. He sat down again. Four coffins? Who was the old man? He wondered if the priest had any connection with the pock-marked chimney sweep?

Arriving at the villa, the orderly held the main door for the priest, then led his charge down the hall and rapped on the library door. It was opened by Abraham B., who extended his hand in greeting to the priest. "It was very good of you to come in this storm, Father."

The Countess arose from the sofa in front of the fire and came forward. "It is a pleasure to see you, Father, to talk to you again. I hope you will stay to lunch with us?"

"Thank you," said the priest.

"Please, Father, sit here by the fire. I will ask the housekeeper to set another place," said the Countess. When she had returned to the library, Abraham B. added a log to the fire and braced himself for his task. The priest, however, made it easier. Casting a sidelong glance first at the Countess, then at Abraham B., he said, "And why have you asked me to come? What is it I may do for you?"

"Father, could you marry us and bless us?" Abraham B. asked.

"Of course, my son. What date have you in mind?"

"Considering the uncertainties of war, Father, we are most anxious that it be very soon. Tomorrow?"

"Ah, no! I must have time for reading the banns. I appreciate your urgency," the priest said with the suggestion of a smile. "I have observed that when a man and woman decide to be married, they invariably feel it to be urgent, even in peacetime."

"But this is wartime," said Abraham B. His mind was reeling at the thought of delay. Their escape date was the next Saturday. If the priest insisted on reading banns on even one Sunday, their marriage would never take place.

"I am well aware it is wartime," answered the priest, not without a trace of bitterness. He was a Frenchman of whom a German was asking a special favor. "Taking this into consideration," the priest went on, "I will agree to marry you after I have read the banns but once—next Sunday."

"Oh, we are so grateful to you, Father!" The Countess burst out. "You are most understanding!"

Abraham B. did not trust himself to speak. Indeed, there was nothing he could say.

29

The advance units of the greatest assault armada ever planned
put to sea on June 4, only to be recalled because of the severe
weather that had surprisingly sprung up and would endanger
the intricate landings. The ships headed back through stormy
seas to their ports. A quarter of a million troops waited aboard
their ships in the havens of southern England while, on June
5 at Portsmouth, General Eisenhower faced the problem of the
lunar cycle; June 5, 6, and 7 were the only three days in that
month when the tides would be favorable for launching the
invasion at Normandy, the opening phase of Overlord.

On June 5, at 4:15 A.M., Eisenhower made his fateful decision. D day was set for June 6.

A few days prior to the invasion, Rommel, hoping to force
his demands that three S.S. Panzer divisions be put under his
immediate command, had arranged for a personal interview
with Hitler. That meeting was set for June 6. Rommel could
not travel by plane because of the constant Allied air forays
across France and Germany. The trip by automobile would
have afforded him some brief time with his family in Herrlingen
before his meeting with Hitler at Berchtesgaden. He got just as
far as Herrlingen—and no farther.

On June 5 the Allied men-of-war were preparing to steam
across the Channel, their purpose to bombard the French beach
defenses and cut them off from inland support. Because of the
extreme weather and heavy seas, German E boats and other

patrol craft did not put to sea the night of June 5. The ill wind brought at least that advantage for the invaders.

On June 5, at 10:00 A.M. the Fifteenth German Army intercepted a coded Allied message; it directed the French underground to begin active resistance.

At 1:00 A.M. on June 6, German Army Group B's chief of staff was informed that Allied parachute troops had been dropped in various sectors of Normandy. The cumbersome German intelligence apparatus eventually relayed reports that multiple paratroop landings were being made on a wide front. Some of these "troops" were later found to be rubber dummies. Immediately following the paratroop drops, a heavy naval coastal bombardment was commenced.

In the absence of Rommel, his chief of staff, Speidel, had placed Army Group B at battle stations. Two S.S. Panzer divisions, in communication with Army Group B, had been alerted, but it could not be released into action without the approval of the High Command. Only the 21st Panzer Division was under Rommel's direct orders; it moved to a position at Bretteville, south of Caen.

At 5:30 A.M., Speidel was informed that a large Allied flotilla was bombarding the Normandy coastline. He instituted Rommel's defense strategy and ordered the coastal defense fortifications along the sea perimeter into action.

Speidel had reported to Rommel by telephone the events as they occurred. Rommel approved the measures taken by Speidel, then hastily returned to Château La Roche–Guyon, arriving late on the afternoon of the sixth. His scheduled meeting at Berchtesgaden might now be just as well forgotten.

The Allied landings continued despite the bad weather; the winds ranged from 17 to 20 knots, the sea in the Channel ran five-foot breakers, the beaches were ranged with four-foot breaker lines. Sherman tanks were to move ashore at the beach designated Omaha; they were to provide the invaders with much needed firepower against the heavy German defense positions. Twenty-seven tanks were lost in the heavy breaker lines. The first wave of the invading force had to depend on the machine guns and mortar pieces that could be man-hauled to the beach. Poor visibility for bombing caused the thirteen thousand bombs dropped by the Eighth Air Force to fall well behind the massive German coastal defense system.

It had been learned too late that a crack, battle-hardened field division had been transferred that morning from Saint-Lô to the area of Omaha Beach for defense exercises. One of the worse disasters of the war was averted by the sheer tenacity of the American soldiers who dug in and hung on through the pure hell of the counteroffensive.

British and Canadian troops moved onto their assault beaches —Gold, Juno, and Sword—and held magnificently. The first assault troops that landed on Utah were put ashore two thousand yards south of their planned objective; by sheerest good fortune they ran into less opposition than if they had landed at their designated point. The 82nd and 101st paratroop divisions were mistakenly dropped far beyond their target points.

Had Hitler acceded to Rommel's demands for release of the S.S. Panzer divisions, they would have swarmed into the Utah, Omaha, Gold, Juno, and Sword beachheads. But Hitler had refused to release the Panzer reserves. As for Goering's "invincible" Luftwaffe, only a very few of the meager number of planes available ever left the ground.

It soon became apparent to the German High Command that a serious Allied effort was in the making. Hitler at Berchtesgaden ranted in fury, demanded to know all details of the Allied assault. Rommel's battle headquarters found it impossible to assess the military situation during the early hours of the attack; the onslaught was merely known to be general.

Speidel and Rommel repeatedly requested the High Command to release the reserve S.S. Panzer units to support the

Calvados area. General Jodl at Berchtesgaden completely ignored these requests. Instead, he spent hours in telephone conversations with Army Group B and the Commander in Chief West, demanding information for the Fuehrer. In the war room, Keitel and others of the General Staff pored over maps, charts, and special data. Through all this, Hitler raged endlessly in his high-pitched, nervous voice.

At approximately 1:30 P.M., before the High Command was able to determine the actual field conditions at Normandy, Hitler stomped off for his afternoon nap. Omaha passed from a critical condition to a working beachhead; Utah became filled in with American battle troops; Hitler slept.

And while he slept, Jodl sternly denied Rommel's latest request for the release of the reserve Panzers, promising instead to call him later.

Speidel, in Rommel's name, had already committed the 21st Panzer Corps, the only Panzer unit available to Rommel, to move up the coast from Caen; these mobile armored units were on both sides of the Orne River expecting to counterattack the Allied forces. It was then that American airborne troops were dropped, by error, into the same area. One of the worst decisions made in the field was that of the officer leading the 21st Panzer Corps; he elected to clear his rear area of the American airborne force. This granted the Allies those precious extra hours to build up at Omaha and Utah.

Rommel's plea to Jodl at last bore some result; at 3:00 P.M., two S.S. Panzer divisions were released to Rommel. By then these divisions had to remain immobile until after dusk because of the intense Allied air cover. So far as Rommel was concerned, he had no Panzer counterattack on the beachheads on June 6.

By late afternoon Rundstedt, Commander West, was desperately trying to make clear to Hitler and the German High Command the calamitous situation. He urged that everything available be moved into the breach immediately. He was told, in reply, that the major landing might be in quite a different place.

Reserves, including the massive Fifteenth German Army, had been ordered by the Fuehrer to stand fast at Calais. Hitler, Goebbels, and Himmler still held to the belief that the main attack would occur on or about June 10, weather permitting, at Pas de Calais. Only now was produced the full effect of the extraordinary Allied plan of deception: the radio messages containing false leads broadcast during April and May; the dummy Allied army, a mock-up of painted wood and canvas, which appeared entirely authentic from aerial observation, poised on the southeast coast of England just opposite Calais; the "captured" Allied invasion document that pinpointed the invasion at Calais and set the date at June 10.

The Allies were astounded that the German leaders clung to the false belief for so long after it had become obvious that a huge battle force had been poured into Normandy. Even Allied intelligence had not suspected the degree of fanaticism Hitler, Goebbels, and Himmler could generate within themselves. As in a trance, the three dreamed of their bygone days of glory, their thundering blitzkrieg victories in the unready world of Poland, France, and Norway. And they dreamed of glory yet to come, the victory in just a few days when the German Army under its brilliant warlord would repulse the "main" Allied invasion and cast their enemies into the sea. No, they would not be fooled by this extravaganza at Normandy.

And so, while nineteen German divisions of Hitler's best troops and Panzer forces sat motionless at Pas de Calais, shackled by fanaticism, the beaches of Normandy were won by the Allies. The Thousand Year Nazi Reich, after barely a decade, faced the beginning of the end.

30

Abraham B. scowled at his image in the mirror as he plied his razor with short, irritable strokes. The orderly stood by a window, looking out into the garden. Abraham B. preferred to shave and dress by himself but, since the General had liked the luxury of valet services, they preserved appearances by at least having the orderly present in Abraham B.'s quarters. It irritated Abraham B., more than usual, on this morning of the eighth of June.

Both were acutely aware of an ominous rumble in the distance. The sounds of war had become intensified in the past two days; the three Allied agents had little doubt that the invasion had begun. Rumors were flying among the small household staff, but not one word of reliable news came from any quarter.

"François might at least get us some word," grumbled Abraham B., breaking the silence. "Is he going to come for us on Saturday or not?"

"If he doesn't, you'll have to marry the lady." The orderly spoke lightly, but he watched keenly for his companion's reaction.

Abraham B.'s only response was to cut himself viciously. After a moment he added, "Well, that's done. You can go now."

The orderly turned to leave, filled with an unspoken sense of sympathy for Abraham B. The orderly suspected the depth of involvement of these two people, thrown together by the caprice of fate. The Countess seemed unlike the warped individual pictured for them during their training sessions. Yet, he thought, he had to assume she was dangerous and unreliable. So far she had served very well to protect them, but if Abraham B.'s involvement should pass the narrow bounds of safety, he and the chauffeur would have to take drastic measures; indeed, they had discussed the details only the evening before.

Alone, Abraham B. was lost in thought. He had not missed the implications of the orderly's final comment, nor the penetrating look that went with it. He wondered, with an increasing sense of danger, how much of his real devotion to the Countess he had revealed to his companions.

It was now solely a question of time. The invasion must be under way; the deception, if it had worked, must not be jeopardized. Their task was to remain above suspicion until they were ordered out, and if plans held up that would be soon.

Solely a question of time. The Countess, who had given so much to him, asked only one thing of him. And that he would probably have to deny.

Solely a question of time. If he lived through this sinister nightmare, he would have all the time in the world—to remember, to wonder, to regret.

Abraham B. entered the long hall with the Gothic windows, surveyed its length, and walked its eighty paces. He passed a long, narrow table, scarcely noticing the two photographs it held, one of an attractive young woman, the other of a young priest. A crucifix stood between them. The family from whom the house had been rented was apparently devout.

Abraham B. moved quickly along. He looked outside; the Countess had apparently left the secluded garden. He turned and headed for her suite.

She sat facing the window with the morning light falling upon her; only her face was in shadow. She turned her head toward him, laying it against the high back of her chair.

"What have you been thinking, sitting here so quietly?" he asked.

"Of ways to keep you loving me," she said.

"A needless pursuit," he answered.

He pulled up a small chair and sat beside her.

"How beautiful the fields are today," she said, turning her head away from him, looking out once more. The fields still glistened with dew. "How good it would be to be home with you—"

He could see the sadness in her face. He leaned forward and kissed her cheek. She pressed toward him.

Abraham B. sat quietly and said nothing. His thoughts were abruptly turned by the distant rumble. That sound was an almost constant background now. If he were there, on some disputed beachhead, instead of here, how much simpler life—or death—would be. Then he turned again to the woman beside him. Will I be a fool forever? he thought impatiently. If I do not bring her harm, then—come what may—I will be the most fortunate of men.

Late in the afternoon, tempted by the clear weather, they decided to risk taking a walk. They strolled to their favorite field, but they saw no little children running and playing there; the low-flying planes had stopped that. They followed an unimportant byroad where a line of stately chestnuts would shield them from view in case they heard approaching planes.

They were not the only ones who had ventured out under the dangerous open skies. Suddenly, from under one of the broad chestnuts, a small gray sedan roared out, passing them at high speed, leaving a brief wake of noise. The Countess looked at Abraham B. questioningly. He merely smiled and folded her hand in his.

They stopped to watch the sun as it moved below the horizon. The pattern of the day was unmindful of war. Now, in the shadows of twilight, the sky need not be feared. They turned down a poplar-lined road, hand in hand.

As they approached a small hut, set back a little from the road, they heard the clanging of a cowbell; in the dusk, they saw a young boy milking a cow in the hut. The milk hit the pail in resounding spurts. The boy's head was propped against the cow. The two stood for some time watching him.

The child looked up but seemed untroubled by their presence; he continued with his task. Then, quite suddenly, the boy's head jerked up. He stopped milking and listened. Abraham B. turned. He noticed a low, purple light in the distance. In mere seconds more appeared. As he watched, he saw black shapes moving up the road under the poplars in the semi-darkness.

The boy stood up, tied the cow securely to the inside railing of the hut, and hastily removed her bell's clapper. He placed a wooden top on the milking pail and in a moment was gone toward the farmhouse.

Minutes later, an advance guard of motorcycles roared by. The large black shapes with the small purple lights followed. They seemed to move through the dusk with ghostly ease, one after the other, about a hundred paces apart. The noise was deafening.

"Panzers," said Abraham B.

The Countess said nothing. There was an eerie feeling in the windless air as the loud growl from the Panzer unit filled the evening. She clung to his arm.

It was more than ten minutes before the tank column moved out of sight and the sound died away. Abraham B. reached for the Countess and held her very close until the trembling that shook her body had ceased.

"I know," he said. "I know."

As they walked back they could feel under their feet the broad ruts made by the heavy tanks. The flat country road, once firm to the foot, was now badly cut up. They both knew that their little world was fragile and would not hold together much longer.

31

Four days had passed since the Allies had smashed their assault forces into Normandy. The coastal bombardment had continued, had become even more concentrated. At times the sound of the heavy guns could be heard far into France. It reached Abraham B.'s ears now, eerily borne by the gale.

He woke from his restless sleep with a shudder. Once more a storm was lashing the trees outside the villa.

He climbed from his bed to look out the window. Angry gray clouds were scudding in from the northeast. Was this the day? How could they go in such weather?

And how could he coldly walk out into the storm without a word, leaving the Countess joyously anticipating their wedding in two days? Again he heard the sound of gunfire. What was going on out there in that hell to the west? They had had no news. Were the Allies going forward, holding, falling back? At least they must be holding or the bombardment would not be so steady.

He thought of his two companions. What were they thinking about, how did they feel about their own predicament? It had been quite some time since François had named this as their day of departure, promising to give them instructions. Now the day had come, yet they had had no word from him. Abraham B. dressed hastily and went to find his companions.

The orderly answered his light knock. The chauffeur made room for Abraham B. beside him on the window seat. They could only surmise that the vigilance of the S.S. was so intense that François had found it too risky to make contact with them. The conclusion of this conference, like that of many others the three had held, was that there was nothing they could do but wait.

Abraham B.'s personal discipline was shredding. Now, staring unseeingly out the window, he used the time to take a grip on himself, concealing his mood of anxiety.

He had been standing before the window quietly for several minutes when he became aware of a tiny, black speck moving along the road between the green fields and the sparse woods. He thought to himself that life went on, in spite of the devastating war then raging not too many miles to the west, in spite of the stormy weather.

Presently the black speck became a bicycle with a rider. Some object seemed to hover above the rider's head. It was something of a feat to ride a bicycle at all with such a strong wind blowing.

Following Abraham's B.'s intent gaze, the orderly and the chauffeur began to watch the approaching cyclist with curiosity. Somehow, Abraham B. thought, that figure's familiar.

"Look!" he exclaimed to the others. "Look, a chimney sweep! He's turning into the drive."

The three men watched as the chimney sweep, still some distance away, carefully placed his bicycle against the wall of the villa and began to unload his paraphernalia. They could not have welcomed the appearance of an angel more than this tall, thin figure, clad from head to toe in demon-black. Only Abraham B. felt a deep sadness mingled with his relief. François had come, as he had said he would, but for Abraham B. and the Countess it signaled the end.

For a moment she filled his mind completely. He could see her profile, her smile, her cameo skin, hear her soft voice and laughter, feel her warmth, those things he loved more dearly than his life. And, in the strange fashion in which the mind unites beauty with love, the words of an almost forgotten song from his youth returned:

> Go where the world is young and fair
> And careless roses blow
> And take my laughter with you there
> And all the love that I can spare,
> And love, more than you know.

Dear God, he thought, if only she is not made to suffer!

The chimney sweep had shouldered his short ladder, brushes, and coiled wires, and was striding toward the rear entrance of the villa. His three watchers headed down the back stairs in a reckless impulse of welcome. They caught themselves only when they saw the housekeeper letting François in.

The chimney sweep, gaunt and tall, looked specially created for his calling. His black leather waistcoat wrapped his body tightly, while the hatchet look of his sharp nose in the pock-marked face gave the impression that he was equal to all obstacles and difficulties.

Feigning an errand in the kitchen, the chauffeur and the orderly passed in that direction, not indicating their disappointment at not being able to speak to François. Abraham B. impassively walked down the hall and turned into the library, carefully leaving the door ajar.

He could hear the housekeeper volubly guiding the sweep down the hall, instructing him to work first on the huge fireplace in the main hall. He was curt toward her and did not encourage her endless conversation. The lack of country gossip which she had hoped he would carry obviously disappointed her. The sweep concentrated on his equipment, prepared to do his work.

Carrying a book he had picked up quite at random, Abraham B. followed the pair into the main hall. The sweep had laid his things neatly about and was putting his tall hat tightly down on his head. He sourly eyed Abraham B., although it was not unusual for people to watch a sweep at his work, breaking the monotony of household routine. The housekeeper clapped her hands to her hips and, brooding darkly at Abraham B.'s interruption, walked out of the main hall.

In the distance, Abraham B. could hear the rumble of bombardment that came on the wind across the coastal plain; a nearby dog bayed his indignation at the incomprehensible sounds.

For a time Abraham B. stood at one side of the huge white marble fireplace, waiting patiently for François to communicate. Why was the sweep waiting? The housekeeper had gone to another part of the villa and the two servant girls would not arrive until later in the morning. The Countess was in her rooms. François, with news on the tip of his tongue, continued his humble actions about the great hearth, paying not the least heed to his observer.

Determined not to betray his impatience, Abraham B. seated himself with an elaborately casual air in a mahogany armchair to the left of the fireplace. He opened his book.

The printed words failed to make the slightest impression on his thoughts. He laid the book on his knee and forced himself to focus on the room about him. Deep red velvet drapes over the long windows on his left set off the dark teakwood beams overhead. Reds played again in the thick Oriental rugs that all but covered the oak floor. The furniture was late Empire, its heaviness appropriate to the large room. Two Gobelin tapestries hung one on either side of the doorway to his right, the delicate tones of one portraying a hunting scene, the other a dance. Will he never finish? thought Abraham B.

Out of the corner of his eye, Abraham B. was aware of François's figure in the buttonless, tightly fitted waistcoat, the coil of heavy wire hanging over his shoulder. He sensed that the cold blue eyes glanced at him from time to time, and wished impatiently that François would say what he had come to say, however painful the message. François was wasting the little time that Abraham B. might have left.

François stepped back from the huge fireplace and muttered an almost inaudible sound. He then turned and walked by Abraham B. to his tool box.

He leaned over the small metal box, straightened, and returned past Abraham B., who tried to appear engaged in his book. François spoke quietly. "Twenty-one June." He repeated, "Twenty-one June. Important you and number two and number three hold fast."

Abraham B.'s entire being seemed to fill with relief, with joy. He strained against his impulse to embrace François. Think, he told himself; you have only a few moments with this man.

He remained in his chair. In a low voice, he said, still looking at his book, "How can we get in touch with you?"

"You need not. I shall contact you at least once every three days." François paused, glanced toward the entrance to the large hall, adding. "The fields I can always see. Stand on the higher ground at eleven o'clock in the morning if you want me."

"And the battle? How goes the battle?" Abraham B. asked.

"Pure hell," said the sweep, "but the devil himself will not stop these invaders!"

François was then gone into the chimney like a phantom; he moved almost noiselessly.

Abraham B., who had sat quite still for a long time, now walked toward the huge opening of the fireplace. At the hearth he paused; he could hear François' movements within and saw a few dark specks float down in front of him. He bent forward, stepped across the hearth to one side, looked up and saw François crouched up a foot or two above the opening. In the half-darkness François held up two thumbs. Abraham B. saw him smile for the first time. It was the warm, firm smile of a brave man, and Abraham B. felt at once the invisible bond that can exist between men who share danger.

François shifted his position and, with the typical shrug of the French, moved up the flue. I'll bet, thought Abraham B., he's a damned fine chimney sweep!

32

With fury the wind drove the rain down. The weather had caused almost everything to stop, but not the war and not the wedding.

The housekeeper, the orderly, and the chauffeur bore witness to the simple ceremony that made Abraham B. and the Countess man and wife. The priest, while sedate and serious, was both kindly and gentle. He seemed less remote than during their first encounter. Abraham B. had the distinct impression that his voice implied quotation marks around the name of the General when he spoke it. Abraham B. hoped his teammates did not have the same startling impression. What, he wondered, had the Countess revealed to the priest in her confession? He dismissed the thought. A little more reliance on faith was peculiarly appropriate to this day and this cause.

By early afternoon the household had returned to its usual placid routine. Abraham B. had been astonished that morning at the appearance of large bouquets of flowers throughout the house, even more astonished at the appearance of a magnum of extraordinarily fine champagne. The toast raised by the orderly had a ring of such warmth and sincerity that Abraham B. strongly suspected his comrades knew at least part of his secret. The priest, before departing, bestowed a gratuitous blessing upon them and at the door turned once more to wish them happiness and God's favor.

Rain swept against the land in greater fury. It was one of the worst storms in many years. The sounds of the wind and rain, the bursts of thunder, veiled the rumble and growl of cannon. Even the weather conspired, it seemed, to give them this one day removed from war. They were left alone together to be just a man and a woman, a husband and a wife, two people in love.

33

Several command cars sped away from the Normandy front in the early hours of a new day, their passengers headed for a council of war. The Allied invasion force had assaulted the Normandy beaches only eleven days before. The battle was being carried into the flat fields, the meadows and the hedgerows, along the edges of little streams and rivers—and always in a sludge of mud. The bombardment had created a wide belt of waste and ruin, which made it difficult for the Germans to rally and reinforce their hard-fighting but disheartened troops.

Marshal Rommel raced through the driving rainstorm that drenched the French countryside in those early morning hours. The escort vehicles, throwing wide water wakes across the road, appeared as mere black masses at the front and the rear of the fast-moving column. The recent storms had been the most devastating the Channel country had seen in the last forty years. At his back, the Marshal could hear the guns, sounding like distant thunder in the midst of the storm. He knew there would be terrible losses in the stationary defense Hitler had ordered across the Orne River in a line not far from Caen.

When they had joined up a short time before, Rundstedt and Rommel had hardly spoken to each other. Rommel was aware that Hitler had not changed in the face of the adversity, yet there might still be a chance to convince him of the realities— here in Normandy, at least.

Since the early spring, Rundstedt and Rommel had been urging the Fuehrer to come to the western front. Hitler's movements had long since become last-minute affairs, to offset plans of would-be assassins. Thus, unexpectedly, late on June 16, the

Fuehrer ordered both field marshals to proceed to Margival for a morning conference on June 17.

Rommel was caught completely by surprise. He had been reconnoitering the front during the night, so it was neccessary for him to travel during the early hours of the morning to reach Margival at daybreak.

Margival was the headquarters built originally to accommodate the Fuehrer during the invasion of England. Hitler's private train could have been hidden in a deep railroad cut; but in this latter period when his movements were so diligently concealed, he did not travel the rigid routes prescribed for trains.

The conference was held in bunkers built for the headquarters. Hitler opened the meeting by excoriating his two field marshals over the success of the Allied landings, for which he declared them responsible. He ranted that Cherbourg was to be held as part of his fortress policy. Rommel stated flatly that the idea of fortress defense was strategically impossible, as he had already stated on several occasions long before the Allied invasion. Rommel reviewed the situation, pointed out that the Allies controlled the air and sea approaches, emphasized that their land forces were plainly superior to those that were then available to counterattack.

Hitler's response was to deliver a lengthy screed on the fierce power of the V weapons; finally his words became rambling, vaguely promising the marshals adequate men and material.

During this long, often bombastic monologue, Hitler grew repetitious and frequently incoherent. General Rudolf Schmundt, Hitler's adjutant, interrupted once to prevent Hitler from appearing like nothing more than a babbling madman. When he again became incoherent on the subject of his V weapons, jet planes, and other secret "miracle weapons," General Schmundt interrupted for the second time, suggesting that Hitler should actually go to the front in the next few days.

Hitler accepted this suggestion, and General von Stuelpnagel was ordered to arrange security for a visit by Hitler to Rommel.

This suggestion out of the way, Hitler resumed his monologue, now lying outright by telling the field marshals that the situation on the Russian front had improved. Again, for the third time, he became almost incoherent, describing what devastating effect the V-1 weapon would have on the English.

Gone was the hypnotic aplomb of his earlier days. Now his arm jerked and twitched like a man with a severe nervous disease. He was pale and obviously not under his own control. After his light, vegetarian lunch, he was observed taking a variety of pills.

When Allied aircraft began bombing the Margival district, the conference was resumed in a deep bomb shelter close by. There Rommel and Rundstedt informed Hitler that they no longer believed the Allies would make their second landing at Calais as had been expected. If Hitler insisted on continuing the war, Rommel urgently required that the troops of the Fifteenth Army be released to him.

The Fifteenth Army and three divisions of the Panzer Corps were still anchored in the Calais-Abbeville area in accordance with Hitler's continuing belief that the landings on the Calvados coast were a feint and that the main attack would eventually be struck in the Calais area.

Rommel continued to say that in his opinion it was no longer necessary for the Allies to execute the second landing expected by the High Command. With the large reserves of men and material that were still available on English soil, the Normandy gateway, unless quickly closed, would provide all the Allies needed to storm Europe.

Once more he urgently recommended that the Fifteenth Army and the remaining Panzers be relocated south of the Seine for deployment against the attacking enemy forces.

Hitler flatly refused. If the fate of the Third Reich had hung by a thread, it snapped at Margival.

34

The Countess watched Abraham B. pour coffee into their cups. Just a man and wife having breakfast, he thought; I must make this appear an ordinary day, a day not unlike yesterday, not unlike tomorrow. Tomorrow. For them there would be no tomorrow. Earlier, in the dark hours of morning, he had met with François. Time had at last run out.

The ten days of their marriage had been a strange island of happiness in a sea of hazard and violence. Both of them were intensely aware of that sea and knew it would soon burst in upon them. But in this fragment of time, all they might ever have, they chose to dwell on their joy. The Countess was recalling a long-past sea journey. She had been young, her companions gay and shipboard life carefree. She talked of the beautiful open sea, and of free and happy hearts. Among her warm descriptions, she told of one morning when she had awakened to greet the dawn. At first she could see only a bank of fog off on the far eastern horizon. Then, in the midst of the gray bank, a glowing shaft of light appeared and expanded, shimmering, as the new day began. Within a minute or so it had fanned out and met a cloud formation in the sky. Sea and sky blended into a dazzling moment of beauty to remember over the years. Beauty can be remembered so well, she said, so well.

Abraham B. listened closely, but his mind raced on, far afield from the beautiful setting she described and the comforting thought she offered with it.

Today was the postponed date François had mentioned—the twenty-first. Abraham B. had slept badly. At dawn he had quietly arisen, dressed, and had gone below to the quarters of the orderly and chauffeur. Neither was there. The rain had momentarily stopped, but a strong wind was howling past the window casements. He went out to the secluded garden, but the chill wind soon drove him back to the main hall of the villa.

He recalled his sense of sudden danger as he noticed a dark figure in the shadows cast by the dying fire. His two companions were gone and here, before him, was a silent stranger. He prepared to meet with the violence that, miraculously, he had thus far escaped. Then the figure moved and the face became visible. François! François was quietly sitting before the small fire looking like a misplaced scarecrow. Immediately sensing Abraham B.'s startled surprise, François motioned him a warning to speak softly.

Tall, pale, and gaunt, clad in his black chimney-sweep garb, François hardly looked like the good shepherd, but that was what he was to Abraham B. The orderly and chauffeur almost at once joined them, reporting that all was quiet in the house and about the grounds. It was then that François outlined the plans for the night.

The hazard had increased because the roads were being closely watched by the Germans. But they had one advantage; the traffic of French civilians moving away from the fighting would be heavier, and those on the move less subject to suspicion.

"You," he had said pointedly to Abraham B., "must not be taken alive. Your fingerprints would mark your end. And it would be a hideous end." François shook his head to emphasize his words. It was quite clear what he meant.

So it was settled. At 11:45 that night. Six miles southwest of the villa. "Be on time, be ready, and please," said François, "be lucky!"

Could that have been only a few hours ago? Abraham B. had not touched his coffee; he was gazing intently at his wife. She reached out her hand across the table, palm up; she wanted his hand to hold. Abraham B. took hers and said nothing. He realized nothing needed to be said. How utterly strange, how incredibly wonderful, he thought; if we lived together for a hundred years we would be no closer, no more wedded than we are now.

The signal was a bird call. It was not more than thirty paces away. A few moments later, Abraham B. looked back over his shoulder. He could hardly make out the villa in the darkness. Only a few moments before he had been able to see it clearly. There was no relief from the demanding pace until, at last, they trudged through a plowed field and then emerged into a little meadow. At the far end Abraham B. saw the huge, dense shapes of poplar trees. And there they entered the little farmhouse.

It had been a hard, nearly straight march for them, on foot and traveling fast for a good hour. Inside the thick brick walls, after every window and door had been shut tightly, a small kerosene lantern was lighted and heavy, white beams became visible overhead. Around the room the three Allied agents saw six men, among them François. On a table in the center of the room, the kerosene lamp burned quite low.

Abraham B.'s memory focused on the old man. Of course— he was the same man who had driven the slow cart bearing the coffin. There in the recesses of the dark room of the small farmhouse, Abraham B. saw the old woman who had followed the cart on foot. The elderly man put on his hat, stepped forward. François said, "Quickly, this way." The light went out and another door opened. He then said, "Across the open area and into the barn. Very quickly, very quietly, please!"

Inside the barn they saw two horse-drawn carts. One had two coffins on it; the one beyond, in the darkness, looked as if it had three.

"Quickly!" whispered François, motioning Abraham B. to the first cart. The lid of the first coffin was pulled back. Then

François said, "You will ride for a mile or so, inside the coffins. It will be not an instant longer than necessary."

The sensation of being inside the coffin with its lid closed down was appalling. Abraham B. felt the cart begin to jounce and realized that it was moving along at a fair pace. The clump of the horses' hoofs and the creaking of the wheels of the cart became the only sound in the world. He felt a mounting sense of panic. It passed. The frequent bumps of the rutted road helped to disturb the extraordinary solitude, the unreality. After a time he was able to accept this strange void; his breathing became regular; his mind was released from the strangeness of his surroundings. And then he remembered and the pain was almost unbearable.

He had waited until she was asleep, then carefully arisen. He had looked at her in the light of the moon that shone fleetingly between passing clouds overhead. How long he gazed at her he did not know. His throat had grown dry. All his rationalizing had been useless; it took a very conscious act of will to make him at last leave her quietly and go to the adjacent dressing room. He had softly closed the door of her room; he remembered how he had almost held his breath, listening. Would she awaken?

He remembered the utterly lost, lonely feeling that overpowered him as he finished dressing in the small room. Then suddenly he heard footsteps in her room. When she called to him, he didn't answer, didn't move. The door had opened slowly, almost reluctantly, as though she hardly dared to open it. She had stood there silhouetted against the moonlight, framed in the open door. He remembered that he could not see her eyes, yet he had known they were searching the dark as his had. He stood there stunned, terrifying thoughts pounding through his mind: no one, no one should know, not even she, least of all she. Then she ran across the small room and into his arms, sobbing. He held her tightly to him.

"I know you are going," she whispered between sobs. He could not answer. "Do not say anything."

Then he remembered how she had whispered, holding back her sobs, only trembling, "Please don't worry, dearest, please don't worry. I knew all along—I knew."

He must cast aside the words she had spoken as though he had never heard them. What did she know? He would not probe. Had he been justified in sparing her, in trusting her? Their orders had been to kill anyone who, by design or accident, discovered the course of their mission. Again a matter of choice, but was there really a choice? Again a question of faith, but was there really any doubt? How long had he known that there was no power on earth that could make him destroy her?

His thoughts returned to the present—he felt the cart turn abruptly, then stop. He could hear the other cart draw alongside; then it, too, stopped. Faint footsteps. The thud of a large door closing. The purring sound of a truck's motor. He felt the coffin being unroped and lifted down; he could hear footsteps and the creak of the cart, which soon faded away. He caught the faint odor of exhaust fumes.

He felt the coffin being jostled about, then come to rest on what he assumed was the bed of the truck; he could feel motor vibrations through the coffin. The heat became intense.

Abraham B. heard two distinct thuds, followed by shuffling, and he sensed the other coffins were being placed on the same truck. Quite abruptly the truck started off. He could almost feel its speed as it ran the remaining miles to their rendezvous, just short of the town of Coulommiers. Dear God, he prayed, protect her now that I cannot. He thought, I have made two vows—one to my country, one to my wife, both before God— and I have broken each. He remembered a line from Thucydides, a quotation from his reading of Latin at school: "Having done what men could, they suffered what men must." He had done what he could.

35

The truck halted by the edge of the road. The coffin lids were thrown aside, the three men stiffly but speedily climbed out and then leaped to the ground. In a moment the truck sped on to Coulommiers with its cargo of empty coffins.

François, four of his men, and the Allied agents raced across the seemingly endless country field until they were nearly a mile from the road. They caught their breath and waited.

Some minutes later the throb of a two-engine bomber could be heard. Soon the motors were cut and only the whine of the wings cutting the air could be heard as the plane descended. In the pale, cloud-misted moonlight they could make out the shape of a plane as it touched down and rumbled along the rough country field. François signaled his companions to crouch out of sight while he moved alone toward the plane to make certain they were not caught in some unexpected trap. The three Allied agents lay still and silent. They had taken endless risks—it would have been madness to take an unnecessary one now. They watched François zigzag off into the darkness and waited in silence in the cold, tall grass for his return.

Abraham B. dug into the ground with his fingers. The earth of France. Farewell.

In a power climb from the long country field, the plane slanted upward into the air and turned, to avoid flying directly over Coulommiers. It climbed into the night and settled on a straight course east, then began slowly to turn back along a wide arc, to throw off spotters trying to determine the plane's point of take-off. The plane cruised in the slow arc for a quarter of an hour and then, its motors opened wide, headed northwest toward England.

She too had made a commitment to the service of her country. She had not relinquished it when she married Abraham B. If he had his secrets, she had hers. It would have been hard to say which of them was the more versed in the ways of espionage, or which the more unwavering.

The Countess knew that she had to be at her destination no later than July 17. On the morning of July 9, as on every other morning when she could do so privately, she telephoned from her rooms in the villa to the Paris office of General von Stuelpnagel. This time she was advised that a car would call for her in the early evening of the eleventh.

The day of departure came and she dreaded leaving the villa. What she loved was no longer there, but the chords of memory seemed to awaken so easily, to echo so sweetly in those quiet rooms.

It was at dusk that her car drew away. She looked back to the villa just before the sudden turn of the little country road. As the car moved on she caught a glimpse of the villa between the lined-up poplars, and then she could see it no more. She turned then and faced the oncoming road. Her destination was Berlin.

36

On July 16, two very pleasant-appearing Gestapo colonels
visited General von Stuelpnagel's office in Paris to question
him about his knowledge of Project 669 and the whereabouts
of the missing German major general. They brought with them
a signed memorandum from Himmler ordering Stuelpnagel to
co-operate to the fullest. The memorandum was the same as
that sent to other high-ranking General Staff officers in various
locations throughout the Third Reich.

The two colonels reported to Himmler their conviction that
General von Stuelpnagel had no present knowledge of the
courier general, had heard nothing from him since the latter
part of June and had assumed that some commission on behalf
of the Fuehrer had taken him away.

Himmler and Goebbels moved into quick conference. They
had sensed trouble when the Gestapo had first reported the
Major General missing from the villa, his departure a complete mystery. But it was the failure of the expected invasion
at Calais to materialize that cast doubt on Project 669. The
whereabouts of the courier general who had delivered the
original document became a matter of vital concern.

Goebbels and Himmler faced one another in deep consterna-
tion. Himmler's veiled but intensive fifteen-day investigation
had yielded no trace of the General. They now accepted as
conclusive what they had for some days suspected: the General
was either a traitor, which was incredible in view of his background, or an Allied impostor, also incredible in view of the

difficulties involved, the foolhardy daring of such a masquerade. Yet the General's disappearance indicated one fact clearly: Project 669 had been a tremendously successful hoax perpetrated by the Allies upon the Germans.

They dared not tell the suspicious Fuehrer about their own grave error in judgment. Nor could they ever inform Keitel or the others in the High Command that 669 had been a hoax. Their reward would have been death—and only a caprice of fate would have granted them a quick and painless end in these final convulsions of Nazi insanity.

Hitler, despondent over the military failures through June and July, had become totally incoherent for long periods. It was no secret in Berlin and Berchtesgaden headquarters that the Fuehrer was a miserable victim of worry and apprehension. It was hazardous, nightmarish for anyone on his staff to give him bad news during this time.

Himmler and Goebbels could not deny the hoax, but they resisted the fantastic idea that an impostor had put it into their hands. Yet no fingerprints of the real General were to be found in the Paris suite or in the villa. Instead, sets of prints of a man unknown to them were found in abundance in both places. A corporal and a lieutenant, aides of the General, were also missing. Their records, when checked, were found to be counterfeit. And so, fantastic as it was, the two deceived conspirators had to accept the fact that the hoax had been carried out by three impostors, three masqueraders.

The two suave colonels who approached Stuelpnagel had also confronted the Countess at her villa. She and the General had actually gone through with a wedding ceremony; this she did not deny.

"But he couldn't have fooled her," Goebbels had protested to Himmler. "How many traitors are we dealing with?"

"I have an idea she'll give herself away. She's in Berlin now."

Himmler looked at the secret file marked Project 669. He added the report on the disappearance of the General and enclosed them both in a folder. Pen poised, he asked, "What shall we call him?"

"Is he American or British?"

"A or B? Who knows."

Himmler wrote "Abraham B." and marked the file closed. He locked it in his personal cabinet and pocketed the key.

Fate seemed determined to conclude the Third Reich in relentless agony. On July 17, Marshal Rommel had met with a near-fatal accident. It happened on the Livarot road, between the two small French towns of Livarot and Vimoutiers in Normandy just three days before Colonel von Stauffenberg's well-timed and carefully planned attempt to kill Hitler at his Rastenburg headquarters in East Prussia. Rommel's near death removed the one man capable of molding an Army revolt. He was taken, severely wounded, to a Luftwaffe hospital in Bernay. Later he was removed from the collapsing Normandy front to another hospital in the interior. No public announcement was made by the High Command; Hitler shunted the blame for the Normandy failure onto Rommel.

By the early evening of July 20, a rumor of stunning impact had spread widely and wildly—the Fuehrer, Adolf Hitler, was dead. A Gestapo report, omitting confirmation of death, acknowledged the attempt at assassination and gave an account of the plot and the plotters. A group of Army generals, aided by others, risked their lives in an attempt to murder Hitler; this, they believed, would end the insane pursuit of a lost cause and stop the annihilation of Germany before it became complete. With Hitler out of the way they would sue for peace and end the war.

At one o'clock on the morning of July 21, Hitler, very much alive, screamed over the German radio his defiance of the "usurpers." It was a long broadcast, which closed with Hitler's promising full vengeance. He kept that promise.

Stuelpnagel's fate was sealed because of his decisive actions in Paris on July 20; he had the whole S.S. force jailed. That same evening, he was ordered to report to Berlin by General Keitel and en route he shot himself. His attempt at suicide blinded him, but he survived and was eventually taken as a prisoner in shackles to Berlin, tried by a German People's Court, and sentenced to death. On August 30, he was hanged.

Later in the year, in October, Rommel was visited at his home in Herrlingen by two of Hitler's adjutants and given his choice of ways of dying. That same day Rommel was dead, a suicide.

Field Marshal von Rundstedt, old and harried, agreed to deliver the eulogy at the state funeral Hitler ordered for Field Marshal Rommel.

Captured Gestapo records later gave the staggering evidence that approximately 7000 arrests were made, allegedly in connection with the attempted assassination, and of those 7000 persons held, some 5000 were put to death.

37

The bright sunlight shone through fourteen tall, wide windows. It was early on a sunny morning in August. A public show, an exhibition, a pageant was in progress. The German People's Court in Munich was in session.

Neither law nor justice played a part in this gory revelry. This was a Nazi spectacle, a fit celebration of a degraded people living under a degenerate philosophy.

The Countess was standing trial for her known participation in the July 20th plot. Himmler himself had prepared the case against her. He carefully avoided any evidence that would connect her with the missing German courier general; the indictment concerned only her involvement with the plot against Hitler. But his investigation, once the broad dimensions of the hoax had become evident, took on a fury and viciousness matched only by its thoroughness. The Countess was subjected to revolting techniques of sophisticated barbarity; so too were certain members of the French underground. That they eventually revealed more than they intended was not surprising; that they resisted for so long was nothing short of astonishing.

The verdict, if such it could be called, was a foregone conclusion. Her death became just one drop in a river of blood that was to leave a scarlet stain straight across the recorded history of humankind—just one lost life among the hundreds, the thousands, the millions lost. The world would go on and time would have its way. Yet one life can mean more to a man than all the world and all of time. And that, perhaps, is his glory.

Such was the story, as best I can recollect and interpret it, that Carlo told to me into the early morning hours. It filled my mind as I prepared for bed and finally drifted into sleep. It returned to my mind almost at once after I had awakened.

Outside my window the view was bleak. The rain continued unabated, as Carlo had predicted it would, and a low-hanging mist, a blanket of thick vapor, obscured much of the distant landscape. There would be no hunting today.

It was almost noon as I dressed hurriedly, hoping to catch Carlo and ask him the many questions that had by now taken distinct form. Those questions remained unanswered. Carlo had, according to Frau Erlot, left word that I be permitted to sleep undisturbed. He had left the lodge quite early and had not mentioned when he would return.

To the best of my knowledge he did not return—not that day or any other day. Carlo had, in a dramatic way, walked off into the mist. When I returned to the lodge on future visits, Carlo was not there, had not returned. My inquiries about him drew little more than a shrug; he had wandered into the area about a year ago and now he had wandered on. For a lone hunter, a remote and quiet man, this was, suggested Erlot, hardly startling behavior. He shrugged again; Carlo, he ventured, was a wanderer.

A wanderer, indeed, I thought, but I wondered if Erlot had any idea of the strange worlds Carlo wandered about. At last I bade Erlot farewell. I never did say good-bye to Carlo.

PART III

Bormann

38

It was in September, sometime after I had last seen Carlo, that my wife, some friends, and I drove to the secluded Bavarian hamlet of Koenigssee.

There was neither hotel nor restaurant in Koenigssee. It was a simple Bavarian mountain village, built to withstand time. Driving in that section of the Tyrol is not easy; the century-old, twelve-foot trackway, cut out of solid rock, was never designed for an automobile. Sunday afternoon added the extra hazard of people strolling along, as their families had on the Sabbath for centuries, to visit in the narrow, winding streets.

Koenigssee was a cluster of white stucco houses of two, three and four stories. A generous number of ash trees, here and there, broke the geometrical patterns of buildings. There was hardly a leaf on the ground despite the season; the hamlet was immaculate and pridefully kept that way. The people seemed a sturdy, square-built lot who lived close to the earth.

We found an old coffee house and sat at the outside tables. This seemed a favorite spot for the townspeople. There was an air of pleasant calm about this drowsy village, lying in the hazy afternoon sun.

We had been there for almost an hour, lazing through our coffee and hard rolls, when suddenly the calm was torn; from far off, shrill sirens pierced the air. We sat stunned, taken completely by surprise. The atmosphere of conviviality, the overtones of laughter, faded away, as these friendly mountain people turned to face the road up from Berchtesgaden.

An American tank column, led by a command car and two

troop carriers moving at maximum possible speed, burst into the village. It was a contingent of the 42nd (Rainbow) Division. As one group of soldiers leaped from their truck and moved down my side of the street, I recognized their commanding officer, a major I knew. He had spotted me and came over at once, a grim expression on his face.

"May I see you for a moment, sir?"

We walked several yards away. Without any amenities, and with the same look of intense seriousness, he said, "I'm sorry. I have to ask you people to leave this area immediately."

"Of course. But what's happened?"

"We have a fairly solid lead that the most wanted war criminal is somewhere around here."

"Can you tell who?" I asked.

"Bormann."

"Bormann?" I repeated. "I understood he had been killed in a railroad yard near Berlin."

"We haven't swallowed that story for some time."

We carried out the major's request and left immediately. As I wished him good luck, he turned a wry face back over his shoulder at me and said, "Slight problem, friend. We haven't a decent notion what this guy looks like. Never had any pictures taken."

As we drove out of the mountains and into the twilight shadowed foothills, my thoughts returned to Carlo's story. I had wondered, in retrospect, how much of it, if any, was true. Carlo had seemed to accept the fact of Bormann's death, all but disdaining any suggestion to the contrary. Yet the opinions expressed by Baron Jesinsky's guests at Kammerschloss, and now this recent incident, seemed to suggest that Carlo was wrong. Perhaps time and the facts revealed by it would resolve the question. For the present I could still speculate on the strange and, for me, utterly compelling, bittersweet adventure of a man I could think of only as Abraham B.

39

Time has its way with us. Rather than affording me an opportunity to pierce the veil surrounding Carlo and his story of the hoax, time removed me from the war-scarred earth of what had been the monstrous Third Reich. My work in Austria completed, I returned to America. But my travels were far from over.

Bending figuratively under the weight of four huge lift-van loads of household equipment and furniture and a new Buick, my wife and I landed in Montevideo, Uruguay, in 1949. It was fate, for it was surely no conscious intention on my part, that brought us there. My new employer, The National City Bank of New York, wanted to familiarize me with the techniques of Latin-American business. As one reflection of the bank's prestige, I was provided with a family membership to the beautiful Montevideo Golf Club. It was there during the next year and a half, while spending leisurely hours on those long, graceful fairways bounded by the waters of the Atlantic and the River Plate, that one more piece of the puzzle was presented to me.

I had made the acquaintance of a number of extremely agreeable German business leaders. Some of these men occupied important posts in South American trade and finance; some were boldly at work rebuilding West Germany and their own delicate but complex personal empires. The horrors of Nazism, which had piled corpses of Jews, Serbs, and Poles to such incredibly hideous heights, were quickly forgotten, vanishing before the merciless realism of world trade.

Although the horrors were overlooked, the less gruesome aspects of Germany in the war and the aftermath were not. Some of the Germans talked in knowing, albeit impersonal, terms about the recent past, about the war criminals, about the German war effort and the invisible hands that had misguided it. Several times there was talk of the escape of Martin Bormann to Red China, and so many references to the "planned-escape possibilities" that I found myself reassessing Carlo's veracity; the substance, if not the details, of what he had told me of the seven escape routes seemed more and more credible. If Carlo had been wrong about Bormann's death yet right about the escape routes, what combination of fact and fancy was woven into his tale of the invasion hoax? The puzzle persisted. For the world it was: In what land—if any—did Martin Bormann live? For me: What truth—if any—was there in the saga of Abraham B.?

After the first or second mention of the Bormann escape to China, I made an effort to pry some additional facts and greater detail from my confidants. Here, however, I met a unanimity of alleged ignorance. No one personally knew any facts; this was all hearsay, gossip, rumor. The more persistent my inquiries, the more remote my sources became. I could understand, of course, that no one wanted to become seriously involved with the question of Bormann; the implications of such a connection could be dangerous as well as ugly.

On only two facts did my informants seem clear and certain, despite their individual inability to suggest evidence to substantiate them. First, Bormann had escaped to China. Second, he arrived there sometime in the early months of 1948.

Curiosity led me to a 1948 yearbook of world events and the entries under China. Data was sparse and none of it, in any way that I could see, was relevant to my point of inquiry. I did note, with some ironic amusement, that 1948, as represented in the Chinese calendar, was 4646, the Year of the Rat.

40

During 1951, I returned to the United States and was engaged in what proved to be a very happy and successful four-year assignment working with public utility companies for the New York firm of Bozell and Jacobs. That assignment finally took me back to California, my home state, in 1954; not long after, I started my own heavy-construction company there in partnership with my brother. I had, at last, come full circle and the days of wandering were over. They had been mostly sunny, exciting, and rewarding. Now my wife and I wanted roots, a place to settle down in, and, for our growing family, a home in the old-fashioned sense.

And so Austria and Carlo, Kammerschloss and its refugees, Koenigssee and Bormann, Hitler and the Third Reich, Abraham B. and the invasion of "Fortress Europe," Uruguay and the seven escape routes, all this became remote and, somehow, took on the raiment of fantasy.

But the fantasy sprang to startling life for me one day in 1959. I had purchased the January 6th issue of *Look* magazine and was skimming it, prior to a more conscientious reading. One article, a combination of text and color photographs, was called "The Insane World of Adolf Hitler." I knew I would return to read the article and I would have continued browsing through the issue, except that one photograph caught my eye.

Carlo, my hunting guide! He was there to the life. My eyes moved at once to the caption; it read, "Hitler called Martin Bormann, murderer, 'my most faithful party comrade.'" Was it possible—Carlo was Martin Bormann?

I devoured the article. Hugo Jaeger, Hitler's photographer, may have had an inkling that there would be a world in which a photograph of Martin Bormann might be a rarity of worth. Or perhaps this was just one of a group of early color photos he had put away and forgotten. In any case, he did not follow Hitler's order to destroy all photographs of Bormann. This picture had been preserved and hidden away. Now it was brought out of hiding.

And now the scattered pieces of the puzzle began to slip together, to merge into a commonsensical, reasonable whole. This did not come clear all at once. The evidence, if I may indulge in legal phrases, is circumstantial; some of it would be inadmissible in a court of law. But the possibility that Carlo and Bormann are one and the same man makes, for the first time, a convincing and compelling case for me.

The preparation of this book has been my attempt to reconstruct a personal experience from the depth of memory and to connect it, at least to my own satisfaction, with the facts we call history. My purpose is to reach—again, to my own satisfaction —some approximation of that elusive quantity, truth.

Truth, whether personal or historical, is a prerequisite to meaning. The closer we approach the fullest measure of truth, the closer, perhaps, we may approach the fullest measure of meaning. Men have not always derived the same apparent meaning from the same apparent truth; it is doubtful that they ever will. Yet the upward course of civilization—and it has been upward despite major regressions to brutish tyranny demonstrated in massive examples by the Nazi dictatorship, the Soviet dictatorship, and the Chinese Red dictatorship—has been highlighted by certain universal recognitions of truth. The pursuit of truth is necessary if men are to live with one another. It is, in a personal sense, equally essential if a man is to live with himself.

I am, then, simply in pursuit of truth. From it I shall hope to find my own meaning. I leave others to find theirs.

I realized at the outset that I am depending very largely upon memory; no description of events, freshly recorded as I experienced them, exists. If such a journal did exist, I would not have attempted this document at all. I have done my best not to use reliance on memory as a license for distortion, but I readily admit the possibility for some inadvertent lapses. They are, I trust, minor.

The section called "The Hoax" has some invention of my own, the inevitable result of a long and intricate story wandering through a man's mind over a decade; under the circumstances, it would be difficult to refrain from dramatizing or even idealizing it. From its very first telling, it was set in my mind as a daring exploit of the Allies. Thus I have told it from the Allied point of view; indeed, I would be capable of telling it in no other way. I admit to filling in small gaps of time and conjuring words that were never spoken; but so did Carlo. He told me a well-rounded narrative, a yarn in the best tradition. I have tried to do no less. What I have added to that section amounts to surprisingly little. The essentials and the overwhelming portion of the details remain as he told them.

This book's content must be judged on its own merit. Yet there are a few points that, by way of a partial summation, ought to be considered. First, the question of Bormann's death. If Bormann died in that last hellish night at Berlin, then he could not have been Carlo. Yet what evidence exists that would lend belief to the reports of Bormann's death?

A number of Germans were, or claim to have been, with the Bormann group fleeing Berlin on the night of its fall. Most of the evidence comes from this body of witnesses—but what do they say? Artur Axmann, the Hitler Youth leader, is the only one who claims to have seen Bormann's body, yet he has supplied at least two contradictory versions of that event. First he claimed he was not with Bormann, but came upon his body under the Pichelsdorf Bridge; the body appeared to have suffered no wounds and Axmann presumed that Bormann, sensing the hopelessness of escape, had committed suicide by taking poison. Next he claimed he was with Bormann crossing the Weidendammer Bridge when Bormann was killed by an exploding shell that had just hit a nearby tank. The conflict in testimony is too apparent to require comment.

Erich Kempka, Hitler's chauffeur, was the first to tell the Weidendammer Bridge story. He claimed that he was walking beside Bormann when the nearby tank was hit and that he, Kempka, was blinded by the explosion. As an afterthought, Kempka added that he had seen Bormann struck and die, but he has never explained just how a blinded man could see anything.

Several other men in the group stated that they *think* Bormann was killed, but all of them agreed that the scene was a shambles of confusion and no one of them claimed either to have seen Bormann hit or to have seen his body. Contradictions, even of this uncertain testimony, exist. One report had Bormann walking beside the tank, another walking behind the tank, another riding inside the tank.

Yet one man in the group, Harry Mengershausen, is positive that Bormann was *not* killed by the exploding shell; he contends that Bormann was in another tank altogether, that Bormann's tank was not damaged and its personnel were not harmed.

Still another member of the group, a Major Tiburtius, stated that the explosion caused such confusion he did not know what happened immediately thereafter, but he claimed he saw Bormann some time later at the Hotel Atlas. By then Bormann was in civilian clothes. Tiburtius further stated that he and Bormann set out together and finally became separated in the Berlin streets. Tiburtius volunteered that Bormann, at that time, had a very good chance to escape. Tiburtius himself got out.

Other reports, little more than hearsay, have been circulated. The Russian forces, at one point, claimed to have discovered

Bormann's body, its head severed from the torso; they asserted they brought the two pieces together, photographed them, and then destroyed the corpse in lime. Yet the photographs were not produced and the claim was never officially authenticated. Furthermore, this story was circulated at the same time that the Russians were claiming, alternatively, that they had Hitler's body, that the British and Americans had Hitler's body, and even that Hitler and his bride, Eva Braun, were alive and in British-American hands. Word from the Russians, as it was before then and has been since, is hardly worthy of serious consideration and surely not of belief.

The most exhaustive study of this entire question was undertaken by H. R. Trevor-Roper, the distinguished historian and Regius professor of history at Oxford, conducting his inquiry with official sanction; his findings were published in 1947 in the book entitled *The Last Days of Hitler*. An appendix was added after ten years, appraising the new information that had come to light in the decade following the war. After a summing-up of all available material regarding Bormann's alleged death, Mr. Trevor-Roper concludes: "Thus the evidence still obliges us to believe that Bormann survived the explosion, and it still does not give the support which Axmann's story requires before we can believe it. If we believe that Bormann is dead, it must be simply because no one has ever produced any acceptable evidence of his existence after 1st May 1945." And he adds, "The fate of Martin Bormann remains a mystery."

A reasonable belief that Bormann was alive in 1946 surely existed at the Nuremberg war-crimes trials. At that time and place, although he was tried in absentia, the evidence against him was sufficient to produce a conviction and a sentence of death.

In September 1947, as I noted earlier, a unit of the 42nd (Rainbow) Division of the United States Army was seriously conducting a search for Martin Bormann in the Tyrol; the records of that unit would so reveal.

Since the end of the war, numerous items concerning the alleged whereabouts of Martin Bormann have been published; in them, he has been reported in Brazil, Chile, Argentina, Spain, Egypt, and the Soviet Union. None of these claims has ever had the slightest demonstrable foundation.

When consulted on March 20, 1963, in Vienna, Simon Wiesenthal, the head of the Center of Documentation, a bureau that has collected much information on Nazi war criminals and helped track down Adolf Eichmann, insisted that he had proof that Martin Bormann had survived World War II.

I submit that, on the basis of what is actually known, Bormann could have survived and escaped from Berlin. If ever a man were equipped to foresee the need for such an escape, if ever a man were constituted to prepare for and execute such a flight, Bormann would be he. I suggest that Bormann did indeed escape.

The next point in question is, quite properly, the photograph in *Look* magazine. How could anyone recognize a man he has not seen in some ten years from a photograph taken, quite possibly, ten years earlier than that? To that I can respond only in this manner: The *Look* reproduction was excellent; the original photograph was clear; and, I believe, it caught Bormann in a characteristic pose. I was with Carlo so many hours and watched him so intently that I would, I think, be difficult to fool. Yet in "The Hoax" the reader is asked to accept the physical substitution of one man by his double. If that is possible, surely it is equally possible for a guide in a Bavarian hunting lodge to appear to be the double of Martin Bormann? Of course it is. But would that guide know such intimate details of the Nazi hierarchy, be so well versed in events that were private to all but the high-ranking few, and have access to the most highly classified intelligence files? That would be stretching mere coincidence well beyond the breaking point. If the possibility exists that Carlo could have been Bormann, and I contend it does, then the striking photographic resemblance between Bormann and Carlo is solid, if not conclusive, evidence to me.

If Bormann could have escaped, if Carlo could have been Bormann, then what, if anything, further supports my contention that he in fact was Bormann?

I thought Carlo a gifted storyteller, but it would require more than a storyteller to have so readily at his command the wealth of ultimately credible detail that Carlo had. Carlo was describing events to me long before any official histories or personal memoirs about the war were published; yet I have failed to discover any single discrepancy between what he told me then, including the historical details of "The Hoax," and the facts as they were described by the most reliable reporters later. Yes, there is one discrepancy. Carlo always skirted the question of Bormann's death, appeared to forward the view that Bormann had died in the rail yards. Under the circumstances, however, Bormann himself would very likely have followed such a course, discreetly suggesting that Bormann was dead and the matter hardly worth further consideration. A prudent man, and Bormann apparently was prudent, would do just as he did. The point I am making is simply this: these events did happen to me and they all fit and make sense *if* Carlo is Bormann. Or, stated another way: these events did happen to me and they remain a mystery *unless* Carlo is Bormann.

But why, one might ask, would so prudent a man have made these disclosures to anyone, even to an American lately upon the scene and quite apparently uninformed? That, I fear, I cannot answer in any conclusive way; I can only guess. It would have been safer, I believe, had Carlo told me nothing. Yet what was he actually risking? At first he told me only those things that were, or could readily be claimed to be, common knowledge to former members of the security police. Only the story of the hoax contained special knowledge that Carlo would have been hard pressed to account for to competent military authority; and by the time Carlo told me that story he had decided to leave. Afterward he quite promptly disappeared. Why, then, tell me the story? My guess is that I may have been too tempting an audience for a master performer. Perhaps he had a touch of vanity that needed an occasional listener. Perhaps he hoped that sometime, long after he could be apprehended, I would reveal what I knew and thus add another chapter to a tale that would have no ending. Or, perhaps, being a man, he just couldn't resist; no man is perfect, not even as a villain. Personally, I think that Bormann told me about the hoax because he was still staggered by what Abraham B. and his two partners had done, because he remained stunned by what the Allies had finally accomplished. Such brilliance in planning, such daring in its execution, he could appreciate and, in his way, applaud. That to me is a possibility within the bounds of reason.

In a final analysis, I am persuaded by the simplicity, the absence of need for contorted reasoning or rationalization, of the Carlo-Bormann explanation of what actually happened to me. Without it, any attempt to explain the known circumstances becomes a tortuous and defeating process.

For me, the puzzle posed in 1947 by Carlo, the hunter, was solved in 1959 by Hugo Jaeger, the photographer. I am convinced, unless and until substantial evidence to the contrary is set forth, that Carlo was Martin Bormann. And since I have no longer any reason to doubt his knowledge, I accept his account of the hoax as substantially true. The reader will, of course, have to make up his or her own mind.

41

The manuscript lay on the table between us. A score or more historical reference books were on a nearby shelf, page-markers awkwardly extended like banners above a miniature paper fortress. An atlas was open to a map of China.

My visitor from the East Coast had been questioning me for almost two hours. He had ticked off the last question of what had, at first, appeared a formidably long and complicated list of inquiries. Neither of us had said anything for several minutes.

"Something wrong?" I asked.

"No, quite the contrary," he replied. "I was just thinking of something you said in the script. You spoke of truth having a meaning, yet you never suggested what this has meant to you."

"Well, that's a fairly large order. Many things have happened over many years and in many places."

"No, I'm not referring to the Carlo-Bormann question; I think I know what that means to you. But you end the script with the statement that you accept the hoax as substantially true. How much of it do you believe?"

I took a deep breath and looked directly at him. "Would it surprise you if I said I believed just about all of it?"

"No," he answered, "it probably would have surprised me if you didn't. But what does it mean to you?"

"Quite a few things, but I'd have to write another book to state them properly. It suggests to me that free men in an open society are capable of more than they realize. That there are men among us, men who love peace and abhor war, who will, without thought of profit or glory or even gratitude, commit themselves to the dark worlds of espionage as a matter of conscience. These may not be heroes in the eyes of the world, but they are gallant men to me. And I think that free men can, acting out of conscience, outreach and outthink those in a closed society acting out of coercion. And that tyranny has the seeds of its own destruction within it—they only need enough time to grow. And that love is a stronger force than hate. That's something of what it means to me."

"And Abraham B.," he said. "What do you suppose it means to him?"

"I've thought about that, and I'll wonder about it for a long time. A very long time."

"So shall I," he said.

POSTSCRIPT

by Ralph Ingersoll

About Ralph Ingersoll

In 1946, Ralph Ingersoll returned home from the European Theatre of Operations in World War II. Mr. Ingersoll, then Lieutenant Colonel Ingersoll, General Staff Corps, Army of the United States, had been a member of the European Invasion Planning Staff; later he was attached to General Omar Bradley's Twelfth Army Group Advance Headquarters. (In between he had landed on D Day with the 82nd Airborne Division.)

Mr. Ingersoll had completed a book dealing with some of his wartime experiences and observations. It was called *Top Secret* and it dealt with the high strategy of both the invasion and the subsequent campaign. At the time, Mr. Ingersoll had purposely left out of his narrative a great many things which were too top-secret for even a book of the same name. One of them was the part he played in the over-all deception operation with which *The Year of the Rat* is concerned. Only when his "professional opinion" of this book was sought did the publishers learn that he had been decorated, by both the United States and the Belgian governments, for his contribution to this operation.

The following is Ralph Ingersoll's postscript to Mr. Zarubica's narrative. It is the opinion of an expert in these matters.

POSTSCRIPT

by Ralph Ingersoll

The editors of Harcourt, Brace & World asked me to read Mr. Zarubica's manuscript because of some things I had told them, years ago, about my own part in mounting Operation Overlord. Operation Overlord was the Allied military designation for the 1944 invasion of continental Europe from the British Isles. The plan for this historic invasion—of which the choice of site and the possible dates for its execution were the most crucial elements—was an all-British effort, to which the American forces, when they arrived in the United Kingdom, accommodated themselves. Mr. Zarubica's extraordinary tale has to do with a hoax perpetrated by British intelligence in support of Operation Overlord.

All of this happened in what was militarily defined as the European Theatre of Operations in World War II. The word "theatre" has always struck me as singularly apt: much of my business *was* ironically theatrical.

In 1943, when Operation Overlord was being mounted in England, I was the first American officer in theatre headquarters made responsible for integrating the activities of the United States forces into what the British called their Cover Plan for Overlord.

A Cover Plan outlines an undertaking aimed at deceiving the enemy as to one's real intentions—usually by substituting a false picture for the real one. Literally, it is designed to cover, as with a mask, what is actually about to happen or is happening. Since the ultimate secrets of Overlord were its time and place, Overlord's Cover Plan concentrated on ways and means of falsifying them.

The cover name for the staff section I set up to aid and abet the British in this nefarious design was simply Special Plans, G-3 (Operations). In it, I not only was indoctrinated into the mysteries of Overlord's Cover Plan, but also worked intimately with my opposite numbers in British intelligence, the men who had dreamed up the whole business and were in charge of its execution. I continued to work with them until I left the theatre after V-E Day.

These are my credentials. Based on them, I was asked what I thought of Mr. Zarubica's narrative.

This is my judgment.

Item A: The over-all picture of high strategy, as it was revealed to Mr. Zarubica, is absolutely correct. Operation Overlord's Cover Plan sought to deceive the Germans by convincing them, first, that the Allies' main effort would be applied at or near the Pas de Calais, where the Channel is only eighteen miles wide, and second, that any landings in far-away Normandy would be diversionary and could be ignored.

Item B: This Cover Plan *was* successful—beyond our fondest dreams. Miraculously, the Germans *did* swallow the phony story, hook, bait, and mortal sinker. It is absolutely true that Hitler held a whole army in reserve back of Calais long after it should have been self-evident that the Normandy landing was the only one there was ever going to be. This force never fired a shot. I was present when it was captured intact by a single United States infantry division (The Big Red First, of course), which intercepted it in the course of retreat at Mons in Belgium. Belatedly, it was trying to get back to Germany after the American Army's breakout from the beachhead. It was in column of march—i.e., not prepared to do battle—and in a hell of a hurry. At the heads of its several convoys were its generals and staff officers (they were in the greatest hurry of all!), slouched down in big, dusty Mercedes-Benzes. One such blunted spearhead of brass actually found itself unexpectedly intruded into a little village where a company of American infantrymen had paused to catch their breath and do their laundry. The whole kit and caboodle of them were captured by the company's clerks and cooks! The United States First Division itself took sixty thousand prisoners in one day!

So the first thing I found extraordinary about the tale told Mr. Zarubica—and what still impresses me most about it—is the over-all accuracy of its background. His hunting guide knew what he was talking about, and it *is* amazing that he knew it in 1946, when it was not available to many historians. Whether he was or wasn't Martin Bormann, he was no ignoramus. He may or may not have fancified his story, but he told it with an authority based on what were top-secret secrets. No minor staff Nazi, escaping from the Allied dragnet, could have known what he did—nor, at that time, could his listener.

Item C: The men who conceived and directed the implementation of the Overlord Cover Plan were capable of engineering such an audacious hoax as that which Mladin Zarubica describes. I worked with many of them, and marveled at both the subtlety and savagery of their imagination, and at the infinite detail with which they embroidered their plots.

As to the particular hoax with which they are here credited, I have no knowledge. But that doesn't rule it out as possibly having happened. A first principle of work in super-secret operations is that one is never told anything one does not *need* to know.

So, in asking myself whether I think it likely that it did happen—the hoax part of the story—I have to fall back on speculation, and salt same with what's left of my "professional" judgment. (After all, I haven't practiced at this kind of deception in many years!)

On balance, I concluded that the talented Carlo took liberties.

It is not that the idea of using a look-alike agent to impersonate a top-flight German general is farfetched. It isn't, at all. In fact, I am certain that if the British planners came across such a coincidence of spit and image, they would have used it —and most likely in the exact way described; i.e., by doing away with the real general and having a whack at substituting their own man—even though, as Abraham B. obviously was, he would most likely be an amateur. He would have to be specially, and laboriously, trained for the part. All this is better than plausible.

It is what the planners did with Abraham B. after they palmed him off on the Germans that stuck in my craw at first. They had him plant a fake operational order for Overlord. I questioned whether they would have. They might have been tempted by opportunity, but they would have been the first to see what they risked, and it seemed a great deal.

You need some background to understand what I've just said.

Item A (again): Overlord's Cover Plan was a very complex operation. It was not an intelligence stunt. It was a very big concept, of great brilliance and of crucial importance, and its implementation was on a very large scale. After all, what it undertook was nothing less than the mass hypnosis of the entire German High Command—and it undertook it successfully. I had to ask myself, "Would those responsible for the Overlord Cover Plan have chanced a miscarriage if the impersonation failed?"

Item B: By spring of 1944 the whole undertaking had been on an operational basis for several months. That is to say that misinformation, in carefully calculated and progressive doses, was already being fed to the German General Staff, using a wide variety of ingenious devices—and the poison had already been observed to be taking effect. As an operation, it was fairly well in hand.

Item C: The Abraham B. hoax *did* risk miscarriage of the whole—because if the Germans had exposed this single piece of monkey business they would have proof that everything else we were doing was monkey business too. The planted fake document is an old trick (as the story itself points out). But if this particular planted document were ever proved false, knowledge of its falseness would give the Germans a blueprint of the truth. They would know, beyond doubt, that the landings would *not* be in the Pas de Calais area—and would see, in startling silhouette, that all the other evidence we'd put forth to this effect was deception. The Cover Plan would have been blown wide open.

But at this point in my analysis I gave myself pause. Was I as certain as I thought I was? Could the planners, instead of risking exposure, have been *counting on it?* Suppose Abraham B. had been caught? (Odds are that he would have been!) Might not the Germans themselves have concluded that the whole adventure had been planned that way—with Abraham B. the expendable patsy—to make them believe that landings at Calais were *out* by sending an agent *certain of capture* to say that they were *in?* The whole business could have seemed too obvious to them; the Germans had high (if still inadequate) respect for the subtlety of their English counterparts. If they were expected to believe that Calais was out, then the *truth* was that Calais was in!

Does *this* theory seem to be based on too devious a thought process? I can assure you that it's not. The double-double-cross was not beyond the capability of even the Wehrmacht's intelligence corps—let alone British intelligence.

Moreover, the planners had other means by which they could have compounded the Germans' dilemma of whether or not to conclude that Abraham B. was or was not a fall guy. If he had been captured, other agents could have let slip the misinformation that he was meant to be captured, that British intelligence had taken his mission's blow-up for granted. The fact that

Abraham B., once apprehended, would surely have revealed himself as an amateur agent would have made it very hard for the Germans to believe that he had been expected successfully to fulfill his apparent mission.

So the planners *might* have figured that they could have their cake and eat it too! If Abraham B. got away with his act (as the narrative tells it)—perfect. If Abraham B. got caught—no harm done, because the Germans would never believe him, and British intelligence could make sure they didn't.

Within the logic of espionage, these are tempting thoughts. Could the British have used their pigeon in a plan that, no matter which way it went, would still serve their purpose?

For one last time: they were quite capable of such ruthless ingenuity.

So in the end, just as Mladin Zarubica advises, the reader is going to have to make up his own mind. In my judgment, this hoax *could* have happened, and the man who revealed it *could* have been Martin Bormann.